G000127775

IMMUNOLOGY AND IMMUNE SYSTEM DISORDERS

ANTIBIOTIC RESISTANCE: ANALYSIS AND MONITORING EFFORTS

IMMUNOLOGY AND IMMUNE SYSTEM DISORDERS

PHARMACOLOGY - RESEARCH, SAFETY TESTING AND REGULATION

IMMUNOLOGY AND IMMUNE SYSTEM DISORDERS

ANTIBIOTIC RESISTANCE: ANALYSIS AND MONITORING EFFORTS

RUFUS FINLEY
AND
MARCOS SOLOMON
EDITORS

Nova Science Publishers, Inc.
New York

For permission to use material from this book please contact us:
Telephone 631-231-7269; Fax 631-231-8175
Web Site: http://www.novapublishers.com

Additional color graphics may be available in the e-book version of this book.

Library of Congress Cataloging-in-Publication Data

ISBN 978-1-61942-416-6

Published by Nova Science Publishers, Inc. † New York

CONTENTS

PREFACE

Infections that were once treatable have become more difficult to treat because of antibiotic resistance. Antibiotics have saved millions of lives, but antibiotic use in food animals contributes to the emergence of resistant bacteria that may affect humans. The Departments of Health and Human Services (HHS) and Agriculture (USDA) are primarily responsible for ensuring food safety.

Chapter 1- Antibiotics have saved millions of lives, but antibiotic use in food animals contributes to the emergence of resistant bacteria that may affect humans. The Departments of Health and Human Services (HHS) and Agriculture (USDA) are primarily responsible for ensuring food safety.

GAO reviewed the issue in 2004 and recommended improved data collection and risk assessment. GAO was asked to examine the (1) extent to which agencies have collected data on antibiotic use and resistance in animals, (2) actions HHS's Food and Drug Administration (FDA) took to mitigate the risk of antibiotic resistance in humans as a result of use in animals, (3) extent to which agencies have researched alternatives to current use practices and educated producers and veterinarians about appropriate use, and (4) actions the European Union (EU) and an EU member country, Denmark, have taken to regulate use in animals and lessons that have been learned. GAO analyzed documents, interviewed officials from national organizations, and visited producers in five states and Denmark.

Chapter 2- Public health experts have expressed concern about an increase in antibiotic resistance among sick patients. Such resistance has been linked to a number of causes, such as overuse of antibiotics by medical professionals and their patients, and their wide use for nontherapeutic (essentially nonmedical) purposes in food animals. Agricultural producers administer antibiotics in feed for some types of food-producing animals not only to treat and prevent diseases, but also to encourage growth and efficient use of feed rations. Some argue that nontherapeutic uses should be severely constrained and/or limited to drugs not associated with human medical treatments. Others oppose this approach, arguing that many animal production operations would not be commercially viable (and that the animals' health could be compromised) without the drugs' routine use, and/or that the linkage between such use and antimicrobial resistance lacks a strong scientific basis.

Chapter 3- Infections that were once treatable have become more difficult to treat because of antibiotic resistance. Resistance occurs naturally but is accelerated by inappropriate antibiotic use in people, among other things. Questions have been raised about whether agencies such as the Department of Health and Human Services (HHS) have adequately assessed the effects of antibiotic use and disposal on resistance in humans. GAO was asked to (1) describe federal efforts to quantify the amount of antibiotics produced, (2) evaluate HHS's monitoring of antibiotic use and efforts to promote appropriate use, (3) examine HHS's monitoring of antibiotic-resistant infections, and (4) describe federal efforts to monitor antibiotic disposal and antibiotics in the environment, and describe research on antibiotics in the development of resistance in the environment. GAO reviewed documents and interviewed officials, conducted a literature review, and analyzed antibiotic sales data.

In: Antibiotic Resistance
Editors: R. Finley and M. Solomon
ISBN: 978-161942-416-6

Chapter 1

ANTIBIOTIC RESISTANCE: AGENCIES HAVE MADE LIMITED PROGRESS ADDRESSING ANTIBIOTIC USE IN ANIMALS*

United States Government Accountability Office

WHY GAO DID THIS STUDY

Antibiotics have saved millions of lives, but antibiotic use in food animals contributes to the emergence of resistant bacteria that may affect humans. The Departments of Health and Human Services (HHS) and Agriculture (USDA) are primarily responsible for ensuring food safety.

GAO reviewed the issue in 2004 and recommended improved data collection and risk assessment. GAO was asked to examine the (1) extent to which agencies have collected data on antibiotic use and resistance in animals, (2) actions HHS's Food and Drug Administration (FDA) took to mitigate the risk of antibiotic resistance in humans as a result of use in animals, (3) extent to which agencies have researched alternatives to current use practices and educated producers and veterinarians about appropriate use, and (4) actions the European Union (EU) and an EU member country, Denmark, have taken to

---

* This is an edited, reformatted and augmented version of The United States Government Accountability Office publication, Report to the Ranking Member, Committee on Rules, House of Representatives GAO-11-801, dated September 2011.

regulate use in animals and lessons that have been learned. GAO analyzed documents, interviewed officials from national organizations, and visited producers in five states and Denmark.

What GAO Recommends

GAO recommends that HHS and USDA (1) identify and evaluate approaches to collecting detailed data on antibiotic use in animals and use these data to evaluate FDA's voluntary strategy, (2) collect more representative data on resistance, and (3) assess previous efforts on alternatives to identify where more research is needed. HHS and USDA agreed with GAO's recommendations.

What GAO Found

HHS and USDA have collected some data on antibiotic use in food animals and on resistant bacteria in animals and retail meat. However, these data lack crucial details necessary to examine trends and understand the relationship between use and resistance. For example, since GAO's 2004 report, FDA began collecting data from drug companies on antibiotics sold for use in food animals, but the data do not show what species antibiotics are used in or the purpose of their use, such as for treating disease or improving animals' growth rates. Also, although USDA agencies continue to collect use data through existing surveys of producers, data from these surveys provide only a snapshot of antibiotic use practices. In addition, agencies' data on resistance are not representative of food animals and retail meat across the nation and, in some cases, because of a change in sampling method, have become less representative since GAO's 2004 report. Without detailed use data and representative resistance data, agencies cannot examine trends and understand the relationship between use and resistance.

FDA implemented a process to mitigate the risk of new animal antibiotics leading to resistance in humans, which involves the assessment of factors such as the probability that antibiotic use in food animals would give rise to resistant bacteria in the animals, but it faces challenges mitigating risk from antibiotics approved before FDA issued guidance in 2003. FDA officials told GAO that conducting postapproval risk assessments for each of the antibiotics approved prior to 2003 would be prohibitively resource intensive, and that pursuing this approach could further delay progress. Instead, FDA proposed a voluntary strategy in 2010 that involves FDA working with drug companies to limit approved uses of antibiotics and increasing veterinary supervision of use. However, FDA does not collect the antibiotic use data, including the purpose of use, needed to measure the strategy's effectiveness.

HHS and USDA have taken some steps to research alternatives to current antibiotic use practices and educate producers and veterinarians on appropriate use of antibiotics. However, the extent of these efforts is unclear because the agencies have not assessed their effectiveness. Without an assessment of past efforts, the agencies may be limited in their ability to identify gaps where additional research is needed. Except for one $70,400 USDA project, all other federal education programs have ended.

Since 1995, the EU, including Denmark, banned the use of antibiotics to promote growth in animals, among other actions. Some of their experiences may offer lessons for the United States. For example, in Denmark, antibiotic use in animals initially decreased following a series of policy changes. The prevalence of resistant bacteria declined in food animals and retail meat in many instances, but a decline in humans has only occasionally been documented. Denmark's data on use and resistance helped officials track the effects of its policies and take action to reverse unwanted trends. The EU faces difficulty collecting data that can be compared across countries, but officials there said such data are needed to fully understand how use in animals may lead to resistance in humans.

ABBREVIATIONS

ADUFA	Animal Drug User Fee Amendments of 2008
APHIS	Animal and Plant Health Inspection Service
ARMS	Agricultural Resource Management Survey
ARS	Agricultural Research Service
CAHFSE	Collaboration in Animal Health and Food Safety Epidemiology
CDC	Centers for Disease Control and Prevention
CIPARS	Canadian Integrated Program on Antimicrobial Resistance Surveillance
DANMAP	Danish Integrated Antimicrobial Resistance Monitoring and Research Program
ERS	Economic Research Service
EU	European Union

FDA	Food and Drug Administration
FSIS	Food Safety and Inspection Service
HACCP	Hazard Analysis and Critical Control Points
HHS	Department of Health and Human Services
MRSA	methicillin-resistant *Staphylococcus aureus*
NAHMS	National Animal Health Monitoring System
NARMS	National Antimicrobial Resistance Monitoring System
NIFA	National Institutes of Food and Agriculture
NIH	National Institutes of Health
NOP	National Organic Program
USDA	U.S. Department of Agriculture
VFD	veterinary feed directive
WHO	World Health Organization

September 7, 2011
The Honorable Louise M. Slaughter Ranking Member
Committee on Rules
House of Representatives

Dear Ms. Slaughter,

Antibiotics have saved millions of lives by controlling infectious diseases, but the continued effectiveness of these drugs is now jeopardized by the emergence of bacteria resistant to antibiotics, according to the World Health Organization (WHO). Antibiotic-resistant infections can result in the use of more expensive drugs for treatment, longer hospital stays, and even death. In addition, the speed at which antibiotic resistance is rendering these drugs ineffective far outpaces the development of new antibiotics, according to WHO. Potential contributors to antibiotic-resistant infections in humans include the widespread use of antibiotics in human medicine, the presence of antibiotics in the environment, and the use of antibiotics in animals raised for human consumption—often referred to as food animals—such as cattle, swine, and poultry.

Antibiotics are an integral part of animal production in the United States and many other countries. According to food animal producers, antibiotic use reduces the cost of producing animals and, therefore, the price consumers pay for food. Antibiotics are used to treat animal diseases; to prevent and control the spread of diseases during phases of production when animals are at an increased risk of illness, such as weaning; and to increase animals' growth rate. Public health officials are particularly concerned about the use of antibiotics to promote growth because such antibiotics are administered in low doses over long periods to large groups of healthy animals, which can cause animals to become reservoirs of antibiotic-resistant bacteria. Once the resistant bacteria develop in food animals, they may be passed to humans through the consumption or handling of meat or other animal-derived food products, contact with animals by farm workers or food processors, or runoff of animal waste into soil or water.

Two federal departments are primarily responsible for ensuring the safety of the food supply, including the safe use of antibiotics in food animals—the Department of Health and Human Services (HHS) and the U.S. Department of Agriculture (USDA). Within HHS, the Food and Drug Administration (FDA) approves for sale, and regulates the manufacture and distribution of, antibiotics used in animals. USDA collects information about antibiotic use and resistance in food animals, funds research related to antibiotic resistance, and educates producers and other users about appropriate antibiotic use.

In April 1999, we reported on federal responsibilities related to tracking and overseeing antibiotic use in food animals and noted that, despite more than two decades of discussion, federal agencies had not reached agreement on the safe use of antibiotics in food animals.[1] We recommended that agencies develop and implement a plan to evaluate the risks and benefits of the existing and future use of antibiotics in agriculture. Subsequently, in 1999, HHS created the Interagency Task Force on Antimicrobial Resistance to coordinate federal efforts to address antibiotic resistance in humans and animals. This task force developed *A Public Health Action Plan to Combat Antimicrobial Resistance* in January 2001 to serve as a blueprint for federal coordination to address antibiotic resistance.

In April 2004, we again reviewed the issue of antibiotic use in food animals and made two recommendations: that FDA expedite its risk assessments of the extent to which antibiotic use in food animals poses a risk to human health, and take mitigating action, if necessary; and that HHS and USDA jointly develop and implement a plan for collecting data on antibiotic use in animals.[2] HHS and USDA generally agreed with our findings, but neither has implemented the recommendations, though both departments continued independent data collection efforts rather than working jointly to develop and implement a plan. Furthermore, we reported that countries in the European Union (EU), in particular Denmark, were taking significant steps to restrict the use of antibiotics in animals and that many countries, including Denmark and Canada, collect detailed data on antibiotic use in animals.

In 2007, we added food safety to our list of high-risk areas that warrant attention by Congress and the executive branch. Our biennial reviews of high-risk issues in 2009 and 2011 concluded that fragmentation of federal food safety oversight continues to be a problem.[3] We have made several recommendations on this issue, including recommending that agencies develop a government-wide performance plan for food safety that includes results-oriented goals and performance measures, as well as information about strategies and resources.[4]

In this context, you asked us to evaluate federal efforts to address risks from antibiotic use in food animals. Our objectives were to determine (1) the extent to which federal agencies have collected data on antibiotic use and resistance in food animals, (2) the actions FDA has taken to mitigate the risk of antibiotic resistance in humans as a result of antibiotic use in food animals, (3) the extent to which federal agencies have conducted research on alternatives to current antibiotic use practices and educated producers and veterinarians about appropriate antibiotic use, and (4) what actions the EU and an EU member country, Denmark, have taken to regulate antibiotic use in food animals and what lessons, if any, have been learned.

In conducting our work, we reviewed documents related to antibiotic use in food animals, including applicable laws; federal plans, regulations, and guidance; and federal reports on antibiotic use, resistance, research, and education. We also interviewed and collected documentation from officials at HHS and USDA. In addition, we conducted structured interviews with representatives of a nonprobability sample of 11 national organizations representing producers of food animals, pharmaceutical companies, and public health organizations. Representatives of these organizations, who spoke on behalf of their members, answered questions about federal efforts to collect data on antibiotic use and resistance, conduct research on alternatives to antibiotics, and educate producers and veterinarians. We selected these organizations because of their expertise in topics surrounding antibiotic use in animals and resistance. Furthermore, we conducted a structured interview of a nonprobability sample of five representatives of national veterinary organizations about federal efforts to conduct research on alternatives to antibiotics and educate producers and veterinarians, as well as any efforts they may have undertaken to address these issues. We sought to include a variety of organizations with perspectives about antibiotic use and resistance;

however, the views of organizations consulted should not be considered to represent all perspectives about these issues and are not generalizable. In addition, we conducted site visits with conventional and alternative (either organic or antibiotic-free) producers of poultry, cattle, swine, and dairy products to obtain a better understanding of production practices; the types of antibiotic use data available at the farm level; and perspectives on federal efforts to educate producers about antibiotics. During these site visits, we also spoke with veterinarians involved with food animal production.

To identify actions the EU and Denmark have taken regarding antibiotic use in food animals, we met with EU and Danish government officials, veterinarians, and producer organizations. We selected the EU and Denmark because they implemented bans on growth promotion uses of antibiotics in 2006 and 2000, respectively, which allows for a review of the effects of these policies in the years since. In addition, we reviewed documents detailing the results of EU and Danish policy actions and interviewed Danish producers and veterinarians at conventional poultry and swine farms to learn about their experiences implementing government regulations on antibiotic use. A more detailed description of our objectives, scope, and methodology is presented in appendix I.

We conducted this performance audit from August 2010 to September 2011, in accordance with generally accepted government auditing standards. Those standards require that we plan and perform the audit to obtain sufficient, appropriate evidence to provide a reasonable basis for our findings and conclusions based on our audit objectives. We believe that the evidence obtained provides a reasonable basis for our findings and conclusions based on our audit objectives.

BACKGROUND

Antibiotics are substances that destroy microorganisms or inhibit their growth; they have been used for 70 years to treat people who have bacterial infections. In this report, the term antibiotic is used to refer to any substance used to kill or inhibit microorganisms, also sometimes referred to as an antimicrobial. Resistance to penicillin, the first broadly used antibiotic, started to emerge soon after its widespread introduction. Since that time, resistance to other antibiotics has emerged, and antibiotic resistance is becoming an increasingly serious public health problem worldwide.

Antibiotic-Resistant Bacteria Can Spread through a Number of Pathways

Bacteria acquire antibiotic resistance through mutation of their genetic material or by acquiring genetic material that confers antibiotic resistance from other bacteria. In addition, some bacteria developed resistance to antibiotics naturally, long before the development of commercial antibiotics. Once bacteria in an animal or human host develop resistance, the resistant strain can spread from person to person, animal to animal, or from animals to humans.

Antibiotic-resistant bacteria can spread from animals and cause disease in humans through a number of pathways (see fig. 1). For example, unsanitary conditions at slaughter plants and unsafe food handling practices could allow these bacteria to survive on meat products and reach a consumer. Resistant bacteria may also spread to fruits, vegetables, and fish products through soil, well water, and water runoff contaminated by fecal matter from animals harboring these bacteria. If the bacteria are disease-causing, the consumer may develop an infection that is resistant to antibiotics. However, not all bacteria cause illness in humans.

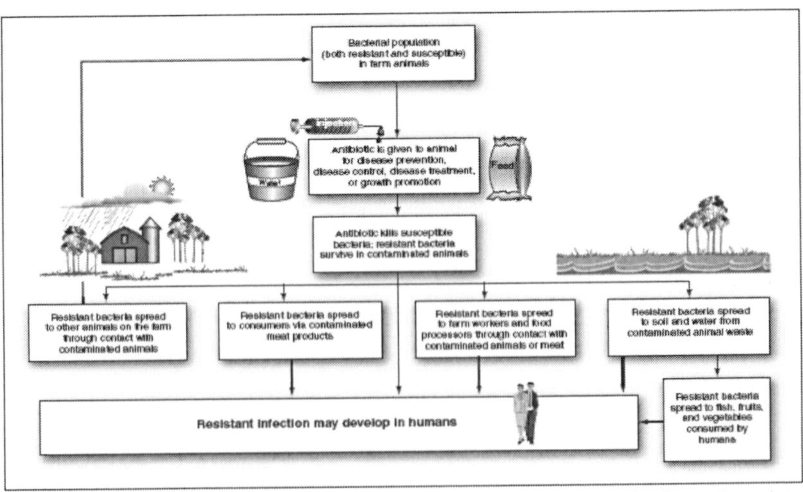

Note: This figure is not intended to represent the full complexity of resistance transmission. For example, antibiotic-resistant bacteria can also be transferred from humans to animals.

Figure 1. Potential Pathways for Spread of Antibiotic-Resistant Bacteria from Animals to Humans.

For example, there are hundreds of unique strains of *Escherichia coli* (*E. coli*), the majority of which are not dangerous. Indeed, while some strains of *E. coli* are dangerous to humans, many *E. coli* bacteria strains are a normal component of human and animal digestive systems.

Antibiotics Are Currently Used in Food Animal Agriculture

The use of antibiotics in animals poses a potential human health risk, but it is also an integral part of intensive animal production in which large numbers of poultry, swine, and cattle are raised in confinement facilities. Over time, food animal production has become more specialized and shifted to larger, denser operations, known as concentrated animal feeding operations. According to a 2009 USDA study, *The Transformation of U.S. Livestock Agriculture: Scale, Efficiency, and Risks*, this shift has led to greater efficiencies in agricultural productivity—meaning more meat and dairy production for a given commitment of land, labor, and capital resources—and lower wholesale and retail prices for meat and dairy products. However, the study notes larger farms with higher concentrations of animals may be more vulnerable to the rapid spread of animal diseases, which producers may combat by using antibiotics. Some producers elect to raise food animals without using antibiotics, in what are known as alternative modes of production (see app. II for more information about alternative modes of production).

Antibiotics provide significant benefits to animal production according to USDA. For food animals, the purposes for which FDA approves the use of antibiotics can be divided into the following four categories:

- *Disease treatment:* administered only to animals exhibiting clinical signs of disease.
- *Disease control:* administered to a group of animals when a proportion of the animals in the group exhibit clinical signs of disease.
- *Disease prevention:* administered to a group of animals, none of which are exhibiting clinical signs of disease, in a situation where disease is likely to occur if the drug is not administered.
- *Growth promotion*: sometimes referred to as feed efficiency, administered to growing, healthy animals to promote increased weight

gain. Such uses are typically administered continuously through the feed or water on a herd- or flock-wide basis. Although such use is not directed at any specifically identified disease, many animal producers believe the use of antibiotics for growth promotion has the additional benefit of preventing disease, and vice versa.

In recent years, both FDA and WHO have sought to identify antibiotics that are used in both animals and people and that are important to treat human infections, also known as medically important antibiotics. Specifically, according to FDA, a medically important antibiotic is given the highest ranking—critically important—if it is used to treat foodborne illness and if it is one of only a few alternatives for treating serious human disease. For example, the fluoroquinolone class of antibiotics is critically important to human medicine because it is used to treat foodborne illnesses caused by the bacteria *Campylobacter* (one of the most common causes of diarrheal illness in the United States), and it is also one of only a few alternatives for treating serious multidrug resistant infections in humans. Some fluoroquinolones are also approved to treat respiratory infections in cattle.

Dairy Production

Source: GAO.

Modern dairy production is diverse, ranging from cows housed indoors year-round to cows maintained on pasture nearly year-round. In the United States, milk comes primarily from black and white Holstein cows genetically selected for milk production. Over the years, the concentration of more cows on fewer farms has been accompanied by dramatic increases in production per cow, arising from improved genetic selection, feeds, health care, and management techniques. Expansion to larger herd sizes has also allowed producers to increase the efficiency of production and capitalize on economies of scale. When a cow is no longer able to breed and produce milk, it is usually sold to the market as beef. According to the National Milk Producers' Federation, dairy producers use antibiotics to treat mastitis, an inflammation of the udder, and other diseases. Any milk produced during antibiotic treatment, and for a specific withdrawal period after treatment has ceased, must be discarded in order to prevent antibiotic residues in milk. This discarded milk imposes an economic cost to dairy producers, so producers generally avoid treating dairy cows with antibiotics when possible. According to the National Milk Producers' Federation, dairy producers do not use antibiotics for growth promotion that are medically important in human medicine.

Several Federal Agencies Have Responsibilities and Authorities Related to Animal Antibiotic Use

Two federal departments are primarily responsible for ensuring the safety of the U.S. food supply, including the safe use of antibiotics in food animals—HHS and USDA. Each department contains multiple agencies that contribute to the national effort to assess, measure, and track antibiotic use and resistance (see table 1).

Table 1. Agencies with Responsibilities Related to Antibiotics in Food Animals

Department	Agency	Contribution to antibiotic resistance efforts
HHS	Centers for Disease Control and Prevention (CDC)	Conducts surveillance[a] and other research to assess the extent of antibiotic resistance and contributes data about antibiotic resistance in humans to the interagency National Antimicrobial Resistance Monitoring System (NARMS), a national public health surveillance system to track antibiotic resistance in foodborne bacteria. Promotes appropriate use of antibiotics in animals through educational activities and training.
	FDA	Approves for sale and regulates the manufacture and distribution of animal antibiotics. Coordinates NARMS (with CDC and ARS) and contributes data about antibiotic resistance in retail meat.
		Conducts research on antibiotic resistance and educates animal antibiotic users about appropriate use.
	National Institutes of Health (NIH)	Conducts research on recognizing, responding to, and circumventing the processes that contribute to antibiotic resistance.
USDA	Animal and Plant Health Inspection Service (APHIS)	Manages the National Animal Health Monitoring System (NAHMS)—a periodic, national survey of producers that focuses on animal health, welfare, and production. Manages the National Veterinary Accreditation Program, which certifies private veterinarians to carry out certain federal animal health programs.
	Agricultural Research Service (ARS)	Conducts research in the food safety and animal health programs on alternatives to antibiotics, and the development, persistence, and transmission of antibiotic-resistant organisms or resistance genes. Contributes data about antibiotic resistance in bacteria from food animals at slaughter plants to NARMS.[b]
	Economic Research Service (ERS)	Conducts the Agricultural Resource Management Survey (ARMS), which principally focuses on farm finances, and their links to farm production practices and management decisions. The survey is also used to track and analyze practices, including antibiotic use, as they relate to food safety and the production and availability of food animals.
	Food Safety and Inspection Service (FSIS)	Inspects slaughter plants, food processing, and import establishments in the United States. Contributes samples collected from food animals or food animal products at slaughter plants as a part of NARMS.

Department	Agency	Contribution to antibiotic resistance efforts
	National Institute of Food and Agriculture (NIFA)[c]	Funds research, education, and extension or outreach activities on antibiotic resistance through grants to universities and other organizations.

Source: GAO.

[a] According to the interagency task force, public health surveillance is the ongoing and systematic collection, analysis, and interpretation of data for use in the planning, implementation, and evaluation of public health practice.

[b] ARS also tests bacteria gathered through NAHMS for antibiotic resistance.

[c] NIFA was formerly known as the Cooperative State Research, Education, and Extension Service.

Both HHS and USDA officials have stated that it is likely that the use of antibiotics in animal agriculture leads to some cases of antibiotic resistance among humans and that medically important antibiotics should be used judiciously in animals.

As mentioned, HHS and USDA agencies participate in the Interagency Task Force on Antimicrobial Resistance, which developed a plan in 2001 to help federal agencies coordinate efforts related to antibiotic resistance. The 2001 interagency plan contains 84 action items organized in four focus areas: surveillance, prevention and control, research, and product development. According to the 2001 interagency plan, public health surveillance, which includes monitoring for antibiotic resistance, is the ongoing and systematic collection, analysis, and interpretation of data for use in the planning, implementation, and evaluation of public health practice. Many of the plan's action items focus on antibiotic use and resistance in humans, and some action items address the use of antibiotics in agriculture, including food animal production, and are directly relevant to this report.

For example, one action item in the surveillance focus area states the agencies' intentions to develop and implement procedures for monitoring antibiotic use in agriculture, as well as in human medicine. Another states that agencies will expand surveillance for antibiotic-resistant bacteria in sick and healthy food animals on farms and at slaughter plants, as well as in retail meat, such as chicken, beef, and pork. The action plan also contains action items related to research on alternatives to antibiotics and providing education to producers and veterinarians about appropriate antibiotic use.

Pork Production

Source: GAO.

The United States is the world's third-largest pork producer and largest pork exporter. Pigs are produced in several types of specialized operations. Farrow-to-finish operators raise pigs from birth to slaughter. In multisite pig production, different phases of production occur at different locations, and breeding pigs are isolated from other pigs at various stages of production. After weaning, pigs move into either a "wean-to-finish" building, where they stay until sent to slaughter, or to a "nursery" building (pictured above) and, 6-8 weeks later, to a "finisher" building until slaughter. According to USDA, the U.S. pork industry has shifted rapidly toward fewer large operations, and operations that specialize in a single phase of production have replaced many farrow-to-finish operations. According to the National Pork Producers' Council, multisite production is designed to keep pigs of the same age together and maximize pig health. Producers minimize disease exposure by keeping pigs in the same groups and thoroughly cleaning barns between herds. However, moving pigs from site to site also presents disease challenges as pigs are exposed to new bacteria from new environments and other animals. Producers may use antibiotics to prevent diseases during vulnerable periods, as well as to treat illnesses. Pork producers may also use antibiotics for growth promotion, particularly when feed costs are high.

Since 2001, HHS and USDA have used the interagency task force to coordinate their activities on antibiotic resistance. For example, each year the task force produces an annual report listing activities completed in that year related to the 2001 interagency plan. The task force recently released a 2010 version of the interagency plan, which is still in draft form but is expected to be finalized this year. The draft 2010 interagency plan contains some new initiatives and also reformulates many of the action items listed in the 2001 plan to be more action-oriented.

AGENCY DATA ARE LIMITED AND RESTRICT EFFORTS TO UNDERSTAND ANTIBIOTIC RESISTANCE

The 2001 interagency plan discusses two types of data needed to understand antibiotic resistance—data on the amount of antibiotics used in food animals ("use data") and data on the level of antibiotic resistance in bacteria found in food animals and retail meat ("resistance data"). Agencies have collected some data to track antibiotic use in animals, but these data lack crucial details identified by the 2001 interagency plan as essential for agencies to examine trends and understand the relationship between use and resistance. To collect data on antibiotic resistance, agencies have leveraged existing programs, but because these programs were designed for other purposes, their sampling methods do not yield data that are representative of antibiotic resistance in food animals and retail meat across the United States. USDA also collected data on both use and resistance in a pilot program that was discontinued.

Agencies Collect Data on Use That Lack Crucial Details

The 2001 interagency plan set a "top priority" action item of monitoring antibiotic use in veterinary medicine, including monitoring data regarding species and purpose of use. The plan stated this information is essential for interpreting trends and variations in rates of resistance, improving the understanding of the relationship between antibiotic use and resistance, and identifying interventions to prevent and control resistance. The task force's draft 2010 interagency plan reiterates the importance of monitoring antibiotic use and sets a goal to better define, characterize, and measure the impact of antibiotic use in animals.

Three federal efforts collect data about antibiotic use in food animals (see table 2). One of these efforts, run by FDA, was created by Congress as a reporting requirement for pharmaceutical companies to provide sales data. The other two efforts are run by USDA agencies and collect on-farm data on antibiotic use by incorporating questions into existing surveys of food animal producers.

Table 2. Current Federal Efforts Collecting Data on Antibiotic Use

Program	Agency	Information collected	Source of information	Frequency of reporting
Animal Drug User Fee Amendments of 2008	FDA	(1) the amount of each antibiotic sold by container size, strength, and dosage form; (2) quantities distributed domestically and quantities exported; and (3) a listing of the target animals, and the approved ways each antibiotic can be used	New Animal Drug sponsors (generally pharma-ceutical companies)	Annual
NAHMS	APHIS	Information about how antibiotics are administered (e.g., in water, feed, or by injection), the number of animals treated, producers' preferred antibiotics for various ailments, and situations when producers would use an antibiotic	Producers	Varies; every 6-7 years for most animal commodities
ARMS	ERS	Information about antibiotic use as a production practice, such as how antibiotic use affects livestock production and farm financial performance	Producers	Varies; approximatel y every 5 years

Source: GAO.

Sales Data

Since our 2004 report,5 FDA has begun to collect and publish data from pharmaceutical companies on antibiotics sold for use in food animals, as required by the Animal Drug User Fee Amendments of 2008 (ADUFA). Under ADUFA, the sponsor of an animal antibiotic—generally a pharmaceutical company—must report annually to FDA: (1) the amount of each antibiotic sold by container size, strength, and dosage form; (2) quantities distributed domestically and quantities exported; and (3) a listing of the target animals and the approved ways each antibiotic can be used (called indications). Section 105 of ADUFA also directs FDA to publish annual summaries of these data. To fulfill this requirement, FDA published the first of these reports on its public Web site in December 2010. (See app. III for examples of antibiotic sales data collected by FDA.) However, to protect confidential business information, as required by statute, FDA's report summarizes the sales data by antibiotic class, such as penicillin or tetracycline, rather than by specific drug and also aggregates sales data for antibiotic classes with fewer than three distinct sponsors.

In submitting the original ADUFA legislation for the House of Representatives to consider, the House Committee on Energy and Commerce stated that it expected these data to further FDA's analysis of, among other things, antibiotic resistance, but the data do not include crucial details that would be needed to do so. Specifically, ADUFA does not require FDA to collect information on the species in which antibiotics are used and the purpose of their use. According to representatives of all the producer and public health organizations we spoke with, because FDA's sales data lack information on the species in which the antibiotic is used, these data do not allow the federal government to achieve the antibiotic use monitoring action item in the 2001 interagency plan, including interpreting trends and variations in rates of resistance, improving the understanding of the relationship between antibiotic use and resistance, and identifying interventions to prevent and control resistance. For example, a representative of one public health organization stated that species-specific data is needed to link antibiotic use in animals with resistance in animals and food. Representatives of most of the public health organizations also stated that the government needs to collect data on the purpose of antibiotic use—that is if the antibiotic is being given for disease treatment, disease control, disease prevention, or growth promotion. Furthermore, representatives of some public health organizations indicated that data on antibiotic use should be integrated with information on antibiotic resistance to allow analysis of how antibiotic use affects resistance. However, a representative of an animal pharmaceutical organization stated that FDA should not attempt to collect national-level antibiotic use data and should instead collect local data to facilitate study of farm management practices in order to help farmers better use antibiotics.

According to FDA officials, sales data can provide an overall picture of the volume of antibiotics sold for use in animals. However, FDA faces several challenges in collecting detailed antibiotic sales data from drug sponsors. First, if an antibiotic is approved for use in multiple species, drug sponsors may not be able to determine how much of their product is used in a specific species. Second, if an antibiotic is approved for multiple purposes, drug sponsors also may not be able to determine how much is used for each purpose. Third, antibiotics may be stored in inventory or expire before they are used, so the quantity sold and reported to the FDA may not equal the quantity actually used in animals. FDA officials acknowledged the limitation of their current sales data and noted that the agency is exploring potential approaches to gather more detailed sales data or other information on actual antibiotic use.

On-Farm Data

Two USDA agencies collect data on antibiotic use from food animal producers by incorporating questions into existing surveys. One of these surveys, managed by APHIS, is the National Animal Health Monitoring System (NAHMS), a periodic, national survey of producers that focuses on animal health and management practices. APHIS staff collect information from producers on how antibiotics are administered (e.g., in water, feed, or injection), what antibiotics they prefer for various ailments, and in what situations they would use an antibiotic. To collect this information, APHIS staff visit farms multiple times over the course of 3 to 6 months and survey producers' practices. Previous NAHMS surveys have examined management practices for dairy cows, swine, feedlot cattle, cow-calf operations, small broiler chicken flocks, and egg-laying chicken flocks, among other species. APHIS officials told us that one of NAHMS' strengths is its national scope and that NAHMS can be used to examine changes in animal management practices, including antibiotic use practices, between NAHMS surveys. However, as we reported in 2004, NAHMS produces a snapshot of antibiotic use practices in a particular species, but the data it collects cannot be used to monitor trends in the amount of antibiotics used over time. According to APHIS officials, these limitations remain today. For example, these officials said that NAHMS is limited by long lag times (approximately 6 years) between surveys of the same species, changes in methodology and survey populations between studies, reliance on voluntary participation by food animal producers, and collection of qualitative, rather than quantitative information on antibiotic use.

Beef Production

Source: USDA.

The United States is the world's largest producer of beef. The beef industry is roughly divided into two production sectors: cow-calf operations and cattle feeding. Beef cattle are born in a cow-calf operation, where both cows and calves are fed grass in a pasture year-round. Once weaned, most cattle are sent to feedlots, where they are fed grain for about 140 days. The beef industry has become increasingly concentrated. According to USDA, feedlots with 1,000 or more head of cattle comprise less than 5 percent of total feedlots in the United States, but market 80 to 90 percent of fed cattle. Weaning, shipping, and processing put stress on cattle and compromise their immune systems. According to the National Cattleman's Beef Association, beef producers use antibiotics to treat common illnesses, including respiratory disease, eye infections, intestinal disease, anaplasmosis (a red blood cell parasite), and foot infections. Some cattle producers also use antibiotics for growth promotion.

Since our 2004 report, USDA's ERS has begun to collect information on antibiotic use through the Agricultural Resource Management Survey (ARMS)—a survey of farms conducted since 1996—though these data have limitations similar to those of NAHMS. ERS uses ARMS data to study how production practices, including antibiotic use, affect financial performance and whether specific production practices can substitute for other production practices. For example, a January 2011 ERS study found that broiler chicken producers who forgo subtherapeutic uses of antibiotics (i.e., use in chickens that are not ill) tend to use distinctly different production practices, such as testing flocks and feed for pathogens, fully cleaning chicken houses between each flock, and feeding chickens exclusively from vegetable sources.

However, like NAHMS, ARMS cannot be used to examine trends in antibiotic use over time because ERS does not resurvey the same farms over time or conduct annual surveys on specific commodities.

According to officials from agencies and some organizations, it is challenging to collect detailed data on antibiotic use in animals from producers for a variety of reasons. First, producers may not always maintain records on antibiotic use. Second, producers who do collect these data may be reluctant to provide them to the federal government voluntarily. FDA is exploring its legal options for requiring producers to report antibiotic use data to FDA. In addition, we observed during our site visits that the types of use data producers collected varied widely. For example, one producer used electronic systems to track all treatments by individual animal, whereas others maintained paper records, and one maintained no records. Also, some food animal species, such as broiler chickens, are generally produced by integrated companies, which own the chickens from birth through processing and contract with a grower to raise them. These growers often receive feed as part of a contract and may not know whether that feed contains antibiotics. For example, one grower we visited did not know that his animals received antibiotics for growth promotion, though the veterinarian from his integrated company indicated that they did. Surveys, such as NAHMS and ARMS, that rely on producers or growers to provide antibiotic use data may be particularly limited by this lack of available data. Moreover, collecting data on-farm from producers is expensive for the federal agencies involved due to the large amount of personnel and time required.

Agencies also face challenges collecting antibiotic use data from other sources. For example, use data gathered from veterinarians may be of limited value because, according to FDA officials, many antibiotics can be purchased without veterinary involvement. In cases where antibiotics do require a prescription, the usefulness of records maintained by veterinarians may vary. For example, one veterinary clinic we visited maintained extensive paper records dating back 2 years, but because they were not electronic, these records would be difficult to analyze. In addition, a veterinary organization we spoke with stated that it would be cumbersome for veterinarians to provide this information to an agency because there is no centralized reporting mechanism, such as an electronic database, for them to do so. According to an official from an organization representing the animal feed industry, feed mills also maintain records on antibiotics mixed into animal feed, including the amount of antibiotic used and the type of feed the antibiotic went into.

Although feed mills do not intentionally track antibiotic use by species, the official said that collectively, this information could be used to track antibiotic use by species. However, FDA officials told us that collecting use data from feed mills would require the development of a new reporting mechanism for these data.

Agencies Are Leveraging Existing Programs to Collect Resistance Data, but These Data Are Not Representative

In 2004, we reported that the federal government collects resistance data through the National Antimicrobial Resistance Monitoring System (NARMS), established in 1996. NARMS is an interagency effort that monitors antibiotic resistance in certain bacteria under three programs: the animal component, led by ARS, samples bacteria from food animals at slaughter plants; the retail meat component, led by FDA, samples retail meat purchased from grocery stores; and the human component, led by CDC, samples bacteria from humans (see table 3). FDA serves as the funding and coordinating agency. From fiscal years 2006 through 2010, the NARMS budget remained constant at $6.7 million, with ARS, FDA, and CDC receiving $1.4 million, $3.5 million, and $1.8 million, respectively. NARMS received a funding increase in fiscal year 2011, to $7.8 million.

Poultry Production

Source: USDA.

The United States is the world's largest poultry producer and second-largest poultry exporter, with broiler chickens—those used for meat—comprising over four-fifths of U.S. poultry production. The broiler chicken industry in the United States is vertically integrated, meaning that the same company—the integrator—generally owns the birds from birth through processing. Integrators contract with local, independent growers to raise the birds, providing chicks, feed, and veterinary services to the grower and visiting each facility regularly to check for health issues. (Above is a picture of broiler chickens in a grower facility.) According to the National Chicken Council, broiler producers may use antibiotics to treat diseases, such as bacterial enteritis (which causes diarrhea in chickens), as well as for growth promotion.

Table 3. Components of NARMS

Agency	Source of bacteria	Bacteria tested for antibiotic resistance
ARS and FSIS	Animals at slaughter plants—chicken, turkey, cattle, swine[a]	Salmonella (chicken, turkey, cattle, swine) Campylobacter (chicken) E. coli (chicken) Enterococcus (chicken)
FDA	Retail meat—samples of chicken breasts, pork chops, ground turkey, ground beef	All 11 participating states[b] culture four products for Salmonella and two products (chicken breast and ground turkey) for Campylobacter.
		4 of these states also culture four products for E. coli and Enterococcus.
CDC	Humans	All 50 states culture for typhoidal Salmonella, non-typhoidal Salmonella, E. coli O157, Shigella 10 states culture Campylobacter[c]

Source: GAO.

[a] ARS also tests bacteria gathered through NAHMS for antibiotic resistance.

[b] FoodNet is a collaborative project between CDC and 10 participating states: California, Colorado, Connecticut, Georgia, Maryland, Minnesota, New Mexico, New York, Oregon, and Tennessee.

[c] In addition, some states culture non-clinical Enterococcus and E. coli. CDC also previously tested Listeria and generic E. coli, but is not currently doing so.

The 2001 interagency plan contains an action item stating agencies will design and implement a national antibiotic resistance surveillance plan. Among other things, the 2001 interagency plan states that agencies will expand and enhance coordination of surveillance for drug-resistant bacteria in sick and healthy animals on farms, food animals at slaughter plants, and retail meat. The plan also states that collecting data on antibiotic resistance will help agencies detect resistance trends and improve their understanding of the relationship between use and resistance. The draft 2010 interagency plan also reiterates the importance of resistance surveillance and includes several action items aimed at strengthening, expanding, and coordinating surveillance systems for antibiotic resistance. According to WHO's *Surveillance Standards for Antimicrobial Resistance*, which provides a framework to review existing antibiotic resistance surveillance efforts, populations sampled for surveillance purposes should normally be representative of the total population—in this case, food animals and retail meat in the United States. Additionally, WHO's surveillance standards state that it is important to understand the relationship of the population surveyed to the wider population, meaning that agencies should understand how food animals and retail meat surveyed in NARMS are similar to food animals and retail meat throughout the United States.

The food animal component of NARMS, led by ARS, gathers bacteria from food animal carcasses at slaughter plants and tests them for antibiotic resistance, but because of a change in sampling method has become less representative of food animals across the United States since we reported in 2004. ARS receives these samples from an FSIS regulatory program called the Hazard Analysis and Critical Control Points (HACCP) verification testing program, which is designed to, among other things, reduce the incidence of foodborne illness. FSIS inspectors work in slaughter plants around the country, where they collect samples from carcasses to test for foodborne pathogens, among other duties. When we last reported on antibiotic resistance in 2004, HACCP verification testing included two sampling programs—a nontargeted program, in which inspectors sampled randomly selected plants, and a targeted program, in which slaughter plants with a higher prevalence of bacteria causing foodborne illness were more likely to be selected for additional sampling. In 2006, FSIS eliminated the random sampling program, which FSIS officials told us has allowed the agency to use its resources more effectively. FSIS now conducts only targeted sampling of food animals in its HACCP verification testing. This nonrandom sampling method means the NARMS data obtained through HACCP are not representative of food animals across the country and cannot be used for trend analysis because bacteria tested by NARMS are now collected at greater rates from slaughter plants that are not in compliance with food safety standards. According to FDA officials, due to this sampling method, the resulting data are skewed for NARMS purposes.

The NARMS retail meat component, led by FDA, collects samples of meat sold in grocery stores and tests them for antibiotic-resistant bacteria, but these samples may not be representative of retail meat throughout the United States. The program began in 2002 and has since expanded to collect retail meat samples from 11 states: the 10 participant states in CDC's FoodNet program, which conducts surveillance for foodborne diseases, plus Pennsylvania, which volunteered to participate in retail meat sampling (See table 3 for the types of bacteria tested). Due to its nonrandom selection of states, FDA cannot determine the extent to which NARMS retail meat samples are representative of the United States. FDA collects bacteria from those states that volunteer to participate in the program, so some regions of the country are not represented in the NARMS retail meat program. According to the FDA Science Advisory Board's 2007 review of NARMS, this lack of a national sampling strategy limits a broader interpretation of NARMS data.[6] According to FDA officials, FDA has not analyzed how representative these samples are of the national retail meat supply in the United States but officials believe that the samples provide useful data that serves as an indicator for monitoring US retail meat.

FDA is aware of the sampling limitations in NARMS and has articulated a strategic goal of making NARMS sampling more representative and applicable to trend analysis in a draft 2011-2015 NARMS Strategic Plan, which was released for public comment in January 2011. The comment period closed in May 2011, and FDA is currently making changes to the plan based on the submitted comments. The plan states that NARMS will become more representative by, among other things, modifying its animal sampling to overcome the biases resulting from the current reliance on HACCP verification testing and improving the geographic representation of retail meat testing, though FDA has not yet planned specific actions to achieve this goal.

According to FDA officials, in light of increased funding for NARMS in 2011, they are exploring ways to improve NARMS sampling to make it more representative. FDA hosted a public meeting in July 2011 to solicit public comment on NARMS animal and retail meat sampling improvements. At this meeting, ARS officials discussed two new on-farm projects—one pilot project, in collaboration with FDA, plans to collect samples from feedlot cattle, dairy cows, and poultry with the goal of evaluating potential sampling sites within the food animal production chain (e.g., on farms or in holding pens at slaughter plants). The second project is in collaboration with Ohio State University and plans to use industry personnel to collect samples from poultry and swine producers. Both projects will test samples for antibiotic resistance through NARMS. Some of the additional suggestions discussed during this meeting included changing FSIS sampling to provide more representative data to NARMS, discontinuing slaughter plant sampling altogether in favor of an on-farm sampling program, and increasing the number of state participants in the retail meat sampling program.

The NARMS human component, led by CDC, collects and tests bacteria from health departments in all 50 states and the District of Columbia. We reviewed the issue of antibiotic resistance and antibiotic use in humans in 2011. This review examined, among other things, the human component of NARMS and concluded that CDC's data is nationally-representative for four of the five bacteria included in the program.[7]

In our interviews, representatives of producer and public health organizations identified several challenges associated with collecting data on antibiotic resistance. First, according to representatives from most public health organizations, ARS, FDA, and CDC are limited by available funding. Sampling and testing bacteria can be expensive, and agencies have to balance competing priorities when allocating resources. For example, in the NARMS retail meat program, FDA could choose to expand retail meat sampling geographically by adding new states to the program, expand the number of bacteria tested, expand the number of samples collected, or expand the types of meat sampled. Second, according to representatives of several producer and public health organizations, agencies may face challenges cooperating and reaching consensus with one another. For example, NARMS reports do not include interpretation of resistance trends across NARMS components. Specifically, while NARMS issues annual Executive Reports that combine data from all three components of NARMS (available on FDA's Web site), these reports do not provide interpretation of NARMS data. According to FDA officials, it is difficult to develop consensus on interpretation for these reports because agencies differ in their interpretations and preferred presentations of NARMS data. Third, according to the FDA Science Advisory Board's 2007 review of NARMS, the lag between NARMS data collection and report issuance can sometimes be excessive. For example, as of August 2011, the latest NARMS Executive Report covered 2008 data. According to FDA and CDC officials, the process of testing bacteria, analyzing and compiling data, and obtaining approval from agencies is time-consuming and increases the lag time of NARMS reports.

In our interviews, representatives of public health organizations also suggested that federal agencies collect additional types of resistance data. First, representatives of several organizations suggested that agencies expand the types of bacteria tested for antibiotic resistance. FDA is aware of this suggestion and has considered whether to add to the types of bacteria it tests. For example, recent studies have discussed methicillin-resistant *Staphylococcus aureus* (MRSA) in retail meat. MRSA is a type of bacteria that is resistant to several antibiotics, including penicillin, and that can cause skin infections in humans and more severe infections in health care settings. In response, FDA is conducting a pilot study to collect data on the prevalence of MRSA in retail meat. However, according to FDA officials, FDA is unlikely to include MRSA in its regular NARMS testing because general consensus in the scientific community is that food does not transmit community-acquired MRSA infections in humans. Second, representatives of three public health organizations suggested that federal agencies link resistance data with data on outbreaks of foodborne illness in humans, which representatives of one organization stated could help scientists document the link between animal antibiotic use and resistant outbreaks of foodborne illness. According to representatives of this organization, NARMS' resistance data are not currently linked to information about foodborne disease outbreaks. According to CDC officials, CDC tests bacteria associated with foodborne illness outbreaks in humans for antibiotic resistance, but does not routinely publish these data.

USDA Discontinued a Program that Collected Data on Both Use and Resistance

When we last reported on antibiotic resistance in 2004, APHIS, ARS, and FSIS collected on-farm use and resistance data from 40 swine producers through the pilot Collaboration in Animal Health and Food Safety Epidemiology (CAHFSE), but this program faced challenges in collecting data and was discontinued in 2006 due to lack of funding. By collecting information from the same facilities over time, agencies could use CAHFSE data to examine the relationship between antibiotic use and resistance. However, according to officials at APHIS and ARS, collecting quarterly on-farm data was burdensome and generated a large number of bacterial samples, which were costly to test and store. Although the agencies wanted to use CAHFSE to monitor antibiotic resistance throughout the food production system, officials from all three agencies told us that this "farm to fork" monitoring raised logistical challenges. For example, FSIS officials examined the feasibility of monitoring resistance data through the slaughter plant but discovered that slaughter plants were reluctant to participate in the program due to fear of enforcement actions and confidentiality concerns. According to APHIS officials, CAHFSE released quarterly and annual data summaries, but it did not issue an overall capping report or formal evaluation of the program.

CAHFSE was discontinued, but NAHMS continues to collect three types of bacteria (*Salmonella*, *Campylobacter*, and *E. coli*) from a subset of surveyed producers and sends them to ARS for antibiotic resistance testing. However, as discussed earlier in this report, NAHMS data provide a snapshot of a particular species but cannot be used to monitor trends. Additionally, as discussed earlier in this report, ARS has started two on-farm projects to collect bacteria from food animals. In one of these projects, which collects samples from poultry and swine, ARS partners with integrated companies to collect a variety of samples from producers. According to an ARS official, because personnel to collect samples were responsible for the majority of costs in the CAHFSE program, using industry personnel rather than ARS staff to collect on-farm samples can significantly reduce the costs of on-farm sampling.

Although data on both use and resistance can be difficult to collect, other countries have been successful in doing so. For example, the Canadian government's Canadian Integrated Program on Antimicrobial Resistance Surveillance (CIPARS), created in 2002, provides an example of on-farm collection of antibiotic use and resistance data. In addition to gathering resistance data similar to NARMS, CIPARS also has an on-farm component, which collects antibiotic use information annually from about 100 swine producers and integrates it with data from resistance testing on fecal samples from the same farms. CIPARS addresses funding limitations by restricting on-farm surveillance to swine, sampling annually rather than quarterly, and collecting slaughter plant samples through industry personnel. A CIPARS official stated that the program's on-farm data could be used to link antibiotic use and antibiotic resistance at the herd level and help identify interventions to prevent antibiotic resistance. CIPARS issues annual reports, which include interpretation of the data such as discussions of trends over time. For example, the most recent report, from 2007, noted an increase in the percentage of bacteria resistant to several antibiotics in samples collected from pigs at slaughter plants from 2003 to 2007.

Denmark also has a use and resistance data collection system, called the Danish Integrated Antimicrobial Resistance Monitoring and Research Program (DANMAP). Data collection covers antibiotic use in food animals and humans, as well as antibiotic resistance in food animals, meat in slaughter plants and at retail, and in humans. The objectives of DANMAP are to monitor antibiotic use in food animals and humans; monitor antibiotic resistance in bacteria from food animals, food of animal origin, and humans; study associations between antibiotic use and resistance; and identify routes of transmission and areas for further research studies.

According to DANMAP officials, Denmark achieves these goals by gathering data on veterinary prescriptions, since all antibiotic use in Denmark is via prescription-only. For veterinary prescriptions, these officials told us Denmark gathers data on the medicine being prescribed, the intended species and age group in which the prescription will be used, the prescribed dose of the antibiotic, the prescribing veterinarian, and the farm on which the prescription will be used. Further, DANMAP collects information on antibiotic resistance in food animals, from healthy animals at slaughter plants and from diagnostic laboratory submissions from sick animals. Denmark also gathers both domestically produced and imported retail meat samples from throughout the country to test for antibiotic resistance. DANMAP officials noted that, in Denmark, the industry is responsible for collecting and submitting bacterial samples from slaughter plants for testing, according to a voluntary agreement, and that the industry spends additional funds to do so. DANMAP issues annual reports, which include interpretation of data on antibiotic use in animals and humans, as well as data on antibiotic resistance in bacteria from food animals, retail meat, and humans. Some DANMAP reports also include more detailed analysis of particular areas of interest. For example, the 2009 DANMAP report examined *E. coli* resistant to penicillins in pigs, retail meat, and humans and found that antibiotic use in both animals and humans contributes to the development of penicillin-resistant *E. Coli*. See appendix IV for more information on DANMAP.

FDA Implemented a Process to Mitigate Resistance Risk for Newer Antibiotics but Faces Challenges with Older Antibiotics

FDA implemented a risk assessment process for antibiotic sponsors, generally pharmaceutical companies, to mitigate the risk of resistance in food animals to antibiotics approved since 2003. However, the majority of antibiotics used in food animals were approved prior to 2003, and FDA faces significant resource challenges in assessing and mitigating the risk of older antibiotics. Instead, FDA has proposed a voluntary strategy to mitigate this risk but has neither developed a plan nor collected the "purpose of use" data necessary to measure the effectiveness of its strategy.

FDA Implemented a Risk Assessment Process to Mitigate Resistance Risk for New Antibiotics

FDA approves for sale, and regulates the manufacture and distribution of, drugs used in veterinary medicine, including drugs given to food animals. Prior to approving a new animal drug application, FDA must determine that the drug is safe and effective for its intended use in the animal. It must also determine that the new drug intended for animals is safe with regard to human health, meaning that there is reasonable certainty of no harm to human health from the proposed use of the drug in animals. FDA may also take action to withdraw an animal drug when new evidence shows that it is not safe with regard to human health under the approved conditions of use.

In 2003, FDA issued guidance recommending that antibiotic sponsors include a risk assessment of any new antibiotics for use in food animals. The guidance is known as *Evaluating the Safety of Antimicrobial New Animal Drugs with Regard to Their Microbiological Effects on Bacteria of Human Health Concern*, Guidance for Industry #152. Under this framework, an antibiotic sponsor would assess three factors: the probability that the resistant bacteria are present in the animal as a consequence of the antibiotic use, the probability that humans would ingest the bacteria in question, and the probability that human exposure to resistant bacteria would result in an adverse health consequence. As part of the third factor, the sponsor considers the importance of the antibiotic to treating human illness, under the assumption that the consequences of resistance are more serious for more important antibiotics. The guidance provides a preliminary ranking of antibiotics considered medically important to human medicine, with the highest ranking assigned to antibiotics deemed "critically important" if it is (1) used to treat foodborne illness and (2) one of only a few alternatives for treating serious human disease. An antibiotic is considered highly important if it meets one of these two criteria. By considering all three factors, the sponsor estimates the overall risk of the antibiotic's use in food animals adversely affecting human health. Though this risk assessment process is recommended by FDA, the antibiotic sponsor is free to prove the safety of a drug in other ways and to consult with FDA to decide if the approach is recommended for its animal antibiotic application. FDA officials said that, in practice, the risk of antibiotic resistance is considered as part of any new animal antibiotic approval.

According to FDA documents, this risk assessment process has been effective at mitigating the risk of resistance posed by new antibiotics because antibiotic sponsors usually consider the risk assessment process in their product development, so the products ultimately submitted for approval are intended to minimize resistance development. Representatives of some producer, public health, and veterinary organizations, as well as an animal pharmaceutical organization, told us that they were generally satisfied with the risk assessment approach. For example, a representative of an animal pharmaceutical organization commented that the risk assessment process was helpful in that it provided a clear road map for drug approvals. Representatives of a veterinary organization said they were pleased that new antibiotics were examined using a comprehensive, evidence-based approach to risk assessment.

However, several organizations also raised concerns. For instance, a representative of an animal pharmaceutical organization said that FDA's risk assessment process was an overly protective "blunt instrument," since FDA would likely not approve any antibiotic product designed for use in feed to prevent or control disease in a herd or flock if the antibiotic is critically important to human health. Representatives from this pharmaceutical organization and a veterinary organization said that FDA's guidance makes it very difficult for antibiotic sponsors to gain approval for new antibiotics for use in feed or water.

In addition, representatives of several public health organizations said that flaws in the criteria FDA used to rank medically important antibiotics may lead the agency to the inappropriate approval of animal antibiotics. For example, they identified a class of antibiotics known as fourth-generation cephalosporins, which are an important treatment for pneumonia in humans and one of the sole therapies for cancer patients with certain complications from chemotherapy. However, since neither of these are also foodborne diseases, under FDA criteria this antibiotic is not ranked as critically important in treating human illness, which these organizations said could lead to the approval of fourth-generation cephalosporins for use in food animals and, eventually, increased antibiotic resistance. FDA officials recently said they intend to revisit the antibiotic rankings to reflect current information. However, FDA officials noted that they believed the current ranking appropriately focused on antibiotics used to treat foodborne illnesses in humans given that the objective of the guidance was to examine the risk of antibiotic use in food animals.

FDA Faces Resource Challenges in Assessing the Risk of Older Antibiotics

According to FDA officials, the majority of antibiotics used in food animals were approved prior to 2003. FDA faces significant challenges to withdraw agency approval, either in whole or in part, of these antibiotics if concerns arise about the safety of an antibiotic. If FDA initiates a withdrawal action because of safety questions that have arisen after an antibiotic's approval, the agency has the initial burden of producing evidence sufficient to raise serious questions about the safety of the drug. Once FDA meets this initial burden of proof, the legal burden then shifts to the antibiotic sponsor to demonstrate the safety of the drug. If, after a hearing, the FDA Commissioner finds, based on the evidence produced, that the antibiotic has not been shown to be safe, then the product approval can be withdrawn.

FDA's 5-year effort to withdraw approval for one antibiotic for use in poultry illustrates the resource-intensive nature of meeting the legal burden to withdraw an approved antibiotic. It is the only example of FDA withdrawing an antibiotic's approval for use in food animals because of concerns about resistance. Specifically, Enrofloxacin, approved in October 1996, is in the critically important fluoroquinolone class of antibiotics, used to treat foodborne illnesses caused by the bacteria *Campylobacter*, and it was used in poultry flocks via the water supply to control mortality associated with *E. coli* and other organisms. In October 2000, based on evidence of increased fluoroquinolone resistance in bacteria from animals and humans, FDA initiated a proceeding to withdraw its approval for the use of two types of fluoroquinolones in poultry. One pharmaceutical company voluntarily discontinued production, but the manufacturer of enrofloxacin challenged the decision. FDA officials told us that it took significant time and resources to gather evidence for the case, even though they had good data showing a correlation between the drug's approval for use in poultry and increasing resistance rates in humans. After an administrative law judge found that enrofloxacin was not shown to be safe for use in poultry as previously approved, the FDA's Commissioner issued the final order withdrawing approval for its use effective September 2005.

FDA officials said that from this case they learned that taking a case-by-case approach to withdrawing antibiotics due to concerns over resistance was time-consuming and challenging. In our 2004 review of federal efforts to address antibiotic resistance risk, we reported FDA was planning to conduct similar risk assessments of other previously approved antibiotics.[8] FDA officials estimated, however, that the enrofloxacin withdrawal cost FDA approximately $3.3 million, which they said was significant. FDA officials told us that conducting individual postapproval risk assessments for all of the antibiotics approved prior to 2003 would be prohibitively resource intensive, and that pursuing this approach could further delay progress on the issue.

FDA Proposed a Voluntary Strategy for Older Antibiotics but Has No Plan to Assess Effectiveness

Instead of conducting risk assessments for individual antibiotics approved prior to 2003, FDA in June 2010 proposed a strategy to promote the "judicious use" of antibiotics in food animals. FDA proposed the strategy in draft guidance titled *The Judicious Use of Medically Important Antimicrobial Drugs in Food-Producing Animals*, draft Guidance for Industry #209. FDA describes judicious uses as those appropriate and necessary to maintain the health of the food animal. The draft guidance includes two principles aimed at ensuring the judicious use of medically important antibiotics. First, that antibiotic use is limited to uses necessary for assuring animal health—such as to prevent, control, and treat diseases. Second, that animal antibiotic use is undertaken with increased veterinary oversight or consultation. To implement the first principle, FDA is working with antibiotic sponsors to voluntarily phase out growth promotion uses of their antibiotics. FDA officials told us they have met with four of the approximately nine major antibiotic sponsors to discuss withdrawing growth promotion uses from their antibiotics' labels and that they plan to engage with generic antibiotic manufacturers in the near future. To implement the second principle of increasing veterinarian oversight of antibiotic use, FDA officials told us that they would like to work with antibiotic sponsors to voluntarily change the availability of medically important antibiotics currently approved for use in feed from over the counter to veterinary feed directive (VFD) status. The majority of in-feed antibiotics are currently available over the counter, but VFD status would instead require these antibiotics to be used with the professional supervision of a licensed veterinarian. In March 2010, FDA issued an advance notice of proposed rulemaking announcing its intention to identify possible changes to improve its current rule on VFDs and seeking public comments on how to do so. FDA officials told us that they received approximately 80 comments by the end of the comment period in August 2010 from interested parties on how to improve the VFD rule, and were taking them into consideration as they drafted the rule, which they hope to publish in 2011. In April 2011, the American Veterinary Medicine Association also formed a new committee to help FDA develop practical means to increase veterinary oversight of antibiotic use.

Representatives of several producer organizations, veterinary organizations, and an animal pharmaceutical organization expressed concern that FDA's focus on ending growth promotion uses would adversely affect animal health. In particular, these representatives said that some animal antibiotics approved for growth promotion may also prevent disease, though they are not currently approved for that purpose. FDA officials said that, in cases where pharmaceutical companies can prove such claims, FDA would be willing to approve these antibiotics for disease prevention. FDA officials emphasized, however, that they do not want companies to relabel existing growth promotion antibiotics with new disease prevention claims with no substantive change in the way antibiotics are actually used on the farm. FDA officials told us they plan to issue additional guidance for antibiotic sponsors to outline a specific process for making changes in product labels.

Furthermore, representatives of several producer and veterinary organizations we spoke with expressed concerns about FDA's efforts to increase veterinary oversight because there is shortage of large animal veterinarians. As we reported in February 2009, there is a growing shortage of veterinarians nationwide, particularly of veterinarians who care for food animals, serve in rural communities, and have training in public health.[9] Additionally, representatives of veterinary organizations said that the paperwork requirements under VFDs are onerous. In particular, this is because VFDs require the veterinarian to deliver a copy of the VFD to the feed producer directly for each VFD, and there are not yet many systems for electronic distribution.

In addition, representatives of several public health organizations expressed concern that FDA's strategy will not change how antibiotics are used for two reasons. First, because FDA is depending on voluntary cooperation to remove growth promotion uses from antibiotic labels, there is no guarantee that pharmaceutical companies will voluntarily agree to relabel their antibiotics. To underline the seriousness of their concerns, in May 2011, several public health organizations filed a suit to force FDA to withdraw its approval for the growth promotion uses of two antibiotic classes (penicillins and tetracyclines). Second, representatives of some public health organizations noted that several medically important antibiotics (six out of eight) currently approved by FDA for growth promotion or feed efficiency are already approved for disease prevention uses in some species (see table 4), which could negate the impact of FDA's strategy.

Table 4. The Overlap between Growth Promotion and Disease Prevention Uses in Food Animal Antibiotics

			Approved uses by animal		
Antibiotic class	FDA ranking of the importance of antibiotic class to human medicine	Antibiotic name	Cattle	Poultry	Swine
Macrolides	Critically important	Tylosin		X	X
		Erythromycin	X	X	X
Lincosamides	Highly important	Lincomycin		X	X
Penicillin	Highly important	Penicillin G Procaine		X	X
Streptogramins	Highly important	Virginiamycin	X	X	X
Tetracyclines	Highly important	Chlortetracycline	X	X	X
		Oxytetracycline	X	X	X
Pleuromutilins	Highly important	Tiamulin			X
Glycolipids	Not ranked	Bambermycins	X	X	X
Polypeptides	Not ranked	Bacitracin	X	X	X
Quinoxalines	Not ranked	Carbadox			X
Ionophores	Not ranked	Monensin	X	X	
		Lasalocid	X	X	
		Laidlomycin	X		

Source: GAO analysis of FDA data.

Note: An "X" indicates FDA approved growth promotion uses, including weight gain and improving feed efficiency. Light gray shading denotes the overlap between antibiotics approved for growth promotion and disease prevention purposes. Boxes in dark gray denote antibiotics not ranked important to human health by FDA.

Because disease prevention dosages often overlap with growth promotion dosages, representatives of one of these organizations said that food animal producers might simply alter the purpose for which the antibiotics are used without altering their behavior on the farm. One veterinarian told us that if FDA withdrew an antibiotic's approval for growth promotion, he could continue to give the antibiotic to the animals under his care at higher doses for prevention of a disease commonly found in this species. The veterinarian stated that there is an incentive to do so because using an animal antibiotic can help the producers he serves use less feed, resulting in cost savings. For example, the in-feed antibiotic may cost approximately $1 per ton of feed, but it can save $2 to $3 per ton of feed, making it an effective choice for the producer.

Although representatives of some producer and public health organizations have raised doubts about the effectiveness of FDA's strategy, FDA does not have a plan to collect the data necessary to understand the purpose for which antibiotics are being used or have a plan to measure the effectiveness of its strategy to encourage more judicious use of antibiotics in animals. FDA officials told us the agency will consider this strategy to be successful when all the growth promotion uses of medically important antibiotics are phased out. FDA officials were unable to provide a timeline for phasing out growth promotion uses, though they identified several next steps FDA intends to take, such as finalizing the guidance document describing their voluntary strategy and issuing additional guidance on its implementation, as well as proceeding forward with the VFD rulemaking process. However, FDA officials stated that the agency had no further plans to measure its progress. In addition, FDA will still allow medically important antibiotics to be used for disease prevention. However, because agency data on sales of antibiotics used in food animals do not include the purpose for which the antibiotics are used, it will be difficult for FDA to evaluate whether its strategy has increased the judicious use of antibiotics or simply encouraged a shift in the purpose of use—for instance, from growth promotion to disease prevention—without lessening use. FDA officials told us the agency is exploring approaches for obtaining additional information related to antimicrobial drug use to enhance the antibiotic sales data that is currently reported to FDA as required by ADUFA, but did not provide a timeline for these efforts.

Agencies Took Steps to Research Alternatives and Educate Users, but Progress Is Unclear

USDA and HHS agencies have taken some steps to research alternatives to current antibiotic use practices and educate producers and veterinarians on appropriate use of antibiotics but the extent of these steps is unclear because neither USDA nor HHS has assessed the progress toward fulfilling the related action items in the 2001 interagency plan.

USDA and HHS Have Conducted Research on Alternatives but Have Not Assessed Progress

An action item in the 2001 interagency plan states that federal agencies will promote the development of alternatives to current antibiotic use, including through research. According to the 2001 interagency plan, such alternatives could include researching vaccines and management practices that prevent illnesses or reduce the need for antibiotic use. However, USDA has not tracked its activities in this area, and neither USDA nor HHS has determined progress made toward this action item.

Since 2001, USDA agencies have undertaken some research related to developing alternatives. However, according to agency officials they are unable to provide a complete list of these activities because USDA's research database is not set up to track research at this level of detail. Instead, research is categorized within the larger food safety research portfolio. In addition, the agencies did not report any activities under this action item in the annual reports published by the interagency task force.

Based on documents provided by USDA and research activities that USDA reported to the interagency task force under other research action items, we identified 22 projects the department funded since 2001 related to alternatives to current antibiotic use practices, with total funding of at least $10 million (see app. V). In addition, ARS officials emphasized that the majority of research performed at ARS related to improving agricultural practices can result in reduced antibiotic needs by producers. Officials from both NIFA and ARS said that they had not assessed the extent to which the research conducted helped achieve the action item in the 2001 interagency plan. Indeed, conducting such an assessment would be difficult without a complete list of relevant research activities. NIFA officials told us that additional funding and resources would be needed to conduct such an assessment, but they did not provide more specific details on how many additional resources would be needed to do so. Although an assessment of research activities on alternatives has not been conducted, ARS officials nevertheless said the agency plans to conduct more research on alternatives to antibiotics in the next 5 years.

Similar to USDA agencies, HHS agencies have conducted some research on alternatives. Specifically, from 2001 through 2005, CDC and FDA sponsored at least five research grants that included funding to research alternatives and reduce resistant bacteria in food animals (see app. VI). NIH has conducted research related to antibiotic resistance that may have applications in both humans and in animals, but agency officials told us that NIH considers human health issues its research priority. Like USDA agencies, HHS agencies did not report any research activities under the action item related to antibiotic alternatives to the interagency task force. No HHS agency has sponsored any such research activities since 2005. HHS officials told us this is because USDA may be the most appropriate lead agency for undertaking alternatives research related to food animals. USDA officials acknowledged that they have a role in researching alternatives to antibiotics, although they said that it is also important for HHS to be involved since FDA would likely be the regulatory agency to approve any products resulting from such research. CDC and FDA officials told us that their agencies have not performed any assessments to determine whether their research activities have helped the agency to fulfill this action item in the 2001 interagency plan.

Representatives of the national veterinary, producer, public health, and animal pharmaceutical organizations that we spoke with told us that greater federal efforts are needed to research alternatives to current antibiotic use in animals. In addition, representatives from most of the veterinary and several public health organizations we spoke with said that the federal government should make greater efforts to coordinate with the food animal industry about researching alternatives to current antibiotic use. Specifically, most representatives from the producer and veterinary organizations emphasized a need for the federal government to provide funding and other resources to the food animal industry for research projects looking at alternatives. For example, representatives from one veterinary organization told us that several national producer and veterinary organizations have goals of utilizing prevention as an alternative to antibiotic use and said that the federal government could help by conducting research on preventive measures such as vaccine development.

The draft 2010 interagency plan includes an action item reiterating that agencies will conduct research on alternatives to current antibiotic use practices, yet USDA and HHS agencies have not evaluated their previous research to determine the extent to which the action item in the 2001 interagency plan was achieved. Without an assessment of past research efforts, agencies may be limited in their ability to identify gaps where additional research is needed. In addition, the draft 2010 interagency plan does not identify steps agencies intend to take to conduct research on alternatives or time frames for taking these steps. In contrast, other action items listed in the draft 2010 interagency plan under the surveillance, prevention and control, and product development focus areas include specific implementation steps illustrating how agencies plan to achieve them. CDC officials told us that the interagency task force agreed not to identify implementation steps until after the final version of the 2010 interagency plan is published, at which time the task force will publish its plans for updating the 2010 interagency plan. In addition, ARS officials said that the interagency task force requested agencies to identify implementation steps that could be accomplished within the next 2 years, and USDA was unable to determine such steps for alternatives research. We have previously reported that evaluating performance allows organizations to track the progress they are making toward their goals, and it gives managers critical information on which to base decisions for improving their programs.10 Tracking progress and making sound decisions is particularly important in light of the fiscal pressures currently facing the federal government.

HHS and USDA Educated Users on Appropriate Use but Have Not Assessed Progress

An action item in the 2001 interagency plan states that federal agencies will educate producers and veterinarians about appropriate antibiotic use. Programs at both HHS and USDA have sought to educate users about appropriate antibiotic use, but the impact of these efforts has not been assessed. In addition, agricultural extension agents and national associations also advise producers on appropriate antibiotic use. The draft 2010 interagency plan no longer has an explicit action item related to appropriate antibiotic use education. There is currently one education activity on appropriate antibiotic use, and after the completion of this effort, there are no plans to develop new education activities.

HHS

HHS agencies sponsored six programs to educate producers and veterinarians about appropriate antibiotic use, the last of which ended in 2010 (see table 5). For example, from 2001 through 2010 CDC funded "Get Smart: Know When Antibiotics Work on the Farm"—also called Get Smart on the Farm—an outreach program that sponsored state-based producer education activities to promote appropriate antibiotic use. CDC officials told us that this was one of the first major education efforts to bring together stakeholders from the public health, veterinary, and agricultural communities to discuss the issue of appropriate antibiotic use. Through the Get Smart on the Farm program, CDC hosted three national animal health conferences designed to foster partnerships between these stakeholders. These conferences included discussions of antibiotic use and resistance in animals. Get Smart on the Farm also funded the development of an online curriculum for veterinary students on antibiotic resistance and appropriate use, which became available in December 2010. CDC officials told us that the agency is planning to take an advisory rather than leadership role in future appropriate use education efforts because they believe that FDA and USDA are the appropriate agencies for leading such efforts. CDC reported that it spent approximately $1.7 million on Get Smart on the Farm activities from 2003 through 2010. Both CDC and FDA officials said that the impact of their education activities had not been assessed. HHS officials also said that they currently do not have plans to develop new activities in the future.

Table 5. HHS Education Activities Related to Appropriate Antibiotic Use from 2001-2011

Agency(s)	Grantee(s) (if applicable)	Project title	Project year(s)	Description of the project
FDA, CDC, NIH	Not applicable	Consumer Education and Outreach Program	2002-2010	National Foundation for Infectious Diseases Annual Conference on Antimicrobial Resistance, which included a public comment meeting on the 2001 interagency plan each year on the last day of the conference.
FDA, CDC	American Veterinary Medical Association	Veterinarian Education and Outreach	2002-2006	Four species-specific booklets that explain appropriate antibiotic use principles were published and distributed to veterinarians; two videos on appropriate use were also produced for veterinary schools.

Table 5. (Continued)

Agency(s)	Grantee(s) (if applicable)	Project title	Project year(s)	Description of the project
CDC	11 states: CO, GA, IA, MI, MN, NE, OH, PA, SC, TN, WA	Get Smart on the Farm: State and Producer Outreach	2001-2010	Sponsored three national animal health conferences where antibiotic resistance and use issues were discussed and funded and developed state-based educational programs to promote appropriate antibiotic use.
	Michigan State University and University of Minnesota	Get Smart on the Farm: Antimicrobial Resistance Learning Site	2001-2010	An online curriculum with pharmacology, microbiology, public health, and species-specific modules.
CDC, FDA, APHIS, FSIS, NIFA	Not applicable	American Veterinary Medical Association Steering Committee on Antimicrobial Resistance	2001-2005	Species-specific antibiotic judicious use principles were developed and published for veterinarians and producers.
FDA, USDA	University of California-Davis	Producer Education Program	2002-2005	Sponsored university-based program that educated producers on antibiotic resistance issues; education materials were distributed to producers by Web-based programs and CD-ROM.

Source: GAO analysis of agency data.

USDA

USDA agencies also sponsored education programs addressing appropriate antibiotic use in animals (see table 6). For example, from 2002 through 2005, USDA agencies worked with FDA to fund university-based programs that sought to educate producers on animal health issues, including antibiotic resistance. From 2006 through 2010 USDA agencies did not report any activities under this action item in the annual reports published by the interagency task force. However, officials noted that education on appropriate antibiotic use remains a priority and that during these years USDA gave presentations at scientific meetings and universities on this topic. USDA officials said the impact of these education efforts was not assessed.

Table 6. USDA Education Activities Related to Appropriate Antibiotic Use from 2001-2011

Agency(s)	Grantee(s) (if applicable)	Project title	Project year(s)	Description of the project
APHIS	Iowa State University	Antibiotic Resistance Continuing Education Learning Module	2011-2012	1 of 19 modules that veterinarians may complete in order to maintain their National Veterinary Accreditation Program accreditation. Expected to be complete and fully integrated into the accreditation program by June 2012.
CDC, FDA, APHIS, FSIS, NIFA	Not applicable	American Veterinary Medical Association Steering Committee on Antimicrobial Resistance	2001-2005	Species-specific antibiotic judicious use principles were developed and published for veterinarians and producers.
FDA, USDA	University of California-Davis	Producer Education Program	2002-2005	Sponsored university-based program that educated producers on antibiotic resistance issues; education materials were distributed to producers by web-based programs and CD-ROM.

Source: GAO analysis of agency data.

The one ongoing USDA appropriate antibiotic use education activity is an APHIS-funded training module on antibiotic resistance currently under development at a cost of $70,400. According to agency officials, the module will be similar to CDC's online curriculum for veterinary students. It will be 1 of 19 continuing education modules for the National Veterinary Accreditation Program, which is designed to train veterinarians to assist the federal government with animal health and regulatory services. The program requires participating veterinarians to periodically renew their accreditations by completing continuing education modules online or at conferences, and participants may elect which APHIS-approved modules to take in order to fulfill their requirements.

Since the APHIS module will be similar to CDC's online curriculum for veterinary students, APHIS officials told us that they will look at CDC's content to determine whether or not to incorporate it into the APHIS-funded module. APHIS officials also told us that they sought out representatives from NIFA, FDA, CDC, the American Veterinary Medical Association, and academic institutions to review the module's content, and expect the training to be available for veterinarians by June 2012. APHIS officials told us that the module on appropriate antibiotic use is not within the National Veterinary Accreditation Program's traditional scope of work. More specifically, APHIS officials are unsure how they would measure the impact of the module because, unlike the other modules in the accreditation program, it is not based on any APHIS regulatory information that can be tracked. That said, officials told us providing antibiotic use education is beneficial and will increase practitioners' awareness in this area. After the completion of the antibiotic use module, USDA officials said they have no plans to develop new education activities.

Additional USDA-funded education activities on appropriate antibiotic use may be conducted through local extension programs. Each U.S. state and territory has a Cooperative Extension office at its land-grant university,[11] as well as a network of local or regional extension offices staffed by one or more experts who provide research-based information to agricultural producers, small business owners, youth, consumers, and others in local communities. NIFA provides federal funding to the extension system, though states and counties also contribute to the program. NIFA provides program leadership and seeks to help the system identify and address current agriculture-related issues. Two producers told us that extension programs are a helpful source of information about animal health issues. For example, they said that extension agents are very helpful in disseminating information, though their impact may be difficult to measure. In addition, they told us that when producers are successful with a preventative practice suggested by an extension agent, neighboring producers may notice and also make similar modifications, creating a multiplier effect.

Two current extension agents also told us they have received inquiries from producers about antibiotic use, although these questions are not necessarily framed as appropriate use. NIFA officials told us that federally funded extension institutions submit an annual plan of work and an annual accomplishment report that provides a general overview of their yearly planned projects based on USDA priorities, but these plans are broad in nature and often do not provide details that allow NIFA to track efforts related to antibiotic use.

Producer and Veterinary Organizations' Perspectives on Federal Education Efforts

Representatives from most of the producer and veterinary organizations that we spoke with said that industry-led efforts are responsible for most of the progress made in educating producers and veterinarians in the last 10 years. For example, the National Cattlemen's Beef Association, National Milk Producers' Federation, and National Pork Board have each developed Quality Assurance programs that advise producers on their views of proper antibiotic use during production. Representatives from most of the organizations we spoke with said that the federal government should have some type of role in educating producers and veterinarians on appropriate antibiotic use, but many—including representatives from all of the producer organizations—said that they believe that these activities should be done in collaboration with industry. Representatives from most of the veterinary and producer organizations also said the federal government could improve collaboration with industry members and groups, and representatives from one veterinary organization pointed to previous federal education efforts to collect and disseminate information about avian influenza as collaborative education efforts federal agencies could model for appropriate use messages.[12] Representatives from this organization noted that such efforts included the federal government and other industry stakeholders working together and disseminating education messages to the public. They also suggested that similar efforts between the federal government, producers, and researchers could be used to educate the industry about appropriate use of antibiotics in food animals.

REGULATION OF ANTIBIOTICS IN THE EU AND DENMARK MAY OFFER LESSONS FOR THE UNITED STATES

Since 1995, the EU and Denmark have taken a variety of actions to regulate antibiotic use in food animals and mitigate the risk such use may pose to humans. Denmark is part of the EU and complies with EU policies but has also taken some additional actions independently. Some of the experiences in the EU and Denmark may be useful for U.S. government officials and producers, though U.S. producers face different animal health challenges and regulatory requirements than European producers.

EU and Denmark Have Taken Action to Regulate Antibiotic Use in Food Animals

From 1995 to 2006, both the EU and Danish governments took a variety of actions to regulate antibiotic use in food animals (see fig. 2). In 1995, Denmark banned the use of avoparcin for growth promotion in food animals, and an EU-wide ban followed in 1997. Avoparcin is similar to the human medicine vancomycin, and some studies suggested that avoparcin use in food animals could be contributing to vancomycinresistant bacteria in humans.[13] Both Denmark and the EU followed up with bans on several additional growth promotion antibiotics, culminating in a total ban on growth promotion antibiotics in 2000 and 2006, respectively. Government and industry officials we spoke with in Denmark emphasized that their bans on growth promotion antibiotics began as voluntary industry efforts that were later implemented as regulations by the government.

EU officials and both industry and government officials from Denmark said the most important factor in the development of their policies was sustained consumer interest in the issue of antibiotic use in food animals and concerns that such use could cause resistance affecting humans. In the face of these concerns, officials explained that EU policies were developed based in part on the precautionary principle, which states that where there are threats of serious or irreversible damage, lack of scientific certainty should not postpone cost-effective measures to reduce risks to humans. Danish industry officials added that, as new data and knowledge arise, it is appropriate to reevaluate the measures taken to reduce risks. We have previously reported that the EU made other food safety decisions based on the precautionary principle, including decisions about inspecting imports of live animal and animal products, such as meat, milk, and fish.[14]

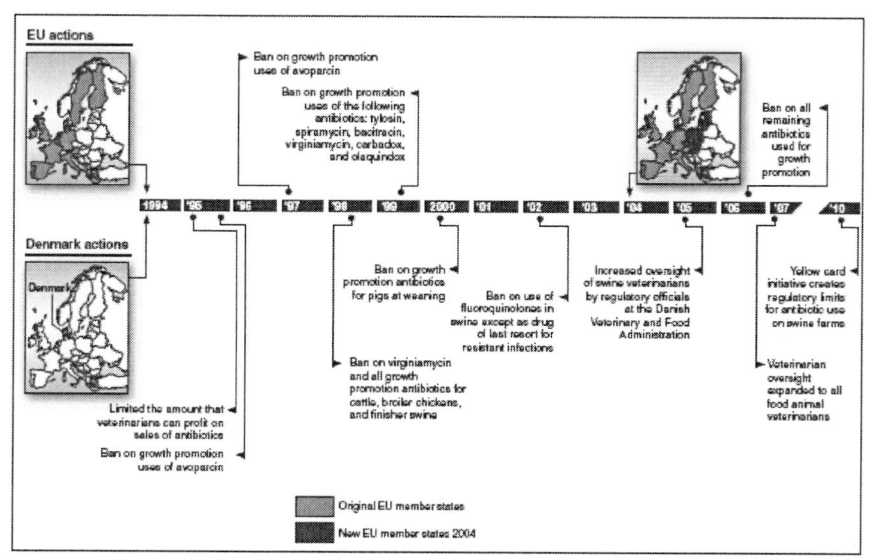

Sources: GAO analysis of EU and Denmark data; Map Resources (maps).

Figure 2. EU and Denmark Actions to Regulate Antibiotic Use in Food Animals, 1994-2010.

According to Danish government officials, Denmark has implemented two additional types of regulations regarding antibiotic use in food animals. First, Denmark has increased government oversight of veterinarians and producers. For example, in 1995, Denmark limited the amount that veterinarians could profit on sales of antibiotics. Then, in 2005, Denmark implemented policies requiring biannual audits of veterinarians who serve the swine industry, which Danish government officials said uses about 80 percent of all food animal antibiotics in Denmark. Government officials said these audits increase veterinarians' awareness of their antibiotic prescription patterns. In 2007 the audits were expanded to cover all food animal veterinarians. Most recently, in 2010, Denmark developed a new system—called the yellow card initiative—which sets regulatory limits on antibiotic use based on the size of swine farms. Swine farms exceeding their regulatory limit are subject to increased monitoring by government officials, which they must pay for. Danish government officials explained that the yellow card initiative is different from their past oversight efforts in that it targets producers rather than veterinarians.

Second, according to Danish government officials, Denmark developed a policy to reduce veterinary use of antibiotics classified as critically important to human medicine by WHO, which like FDA, has a ranking of such antibiotics. For example, in 2002 Denmark limited veterinary prescriptions of fluoroquinolones to cases in which testing showed that no other antibiotic would be effective at treating the disease. In addition, veterinarians prescribing fluoroquinolones to food animals would need to notify government regulatory officials.

EU and Denmark Experiences Suggest Possible Lessons for the United States

U.S. producers face different animal health challenges and regulatory requirements than producers in the EU and Denmark, making it difficult to determine how effectively similar policies could be implemented in the United States. Specifically, industry officials in Denmark explained that several diseases that affect producers in the United States are no longer active in Denmark. For example, broiler chicken producers in Denmark spent many years improving their biosecurity and successfully eradicated *Salmonella*, which can cause disease both in broiler chickens and in humans, and Danish cattle producers do not have to worry about brucellosis, which has not been seen in Denmark in decades. Similarly, the regulatory environment in the EU differs from that in the United States. For example, EU countries develop and implement policies using the precautionary principle. In addition, the EU and Denmark both require prescriptions for the use of most antibiotics in animals, but the United States requires them in certain limited circumstances. Officials from HHS and USDA said they are aware of other countries' efforts to regulate antibiotic use in food animals and participate in international conferences and meetings addressing these issues. Based on the experiences in the EU and Denmark, there are several lessons that may be useful for U.S. government officials and producers.

Denmark's Antibiotic Use Data Allowed Officials to Track How Policy Changes Affected Use in Food Animals and Take Appropriate Response

According to Danish government officials, Denmark's antibiotic use data are detailed enough to allow the country to track trends in use and monitor the effects of their policies. Specifically, data show that antibiotic use in food animals declined from 1994 to 1999, but then it increased modestly from 1999 to 2009, while remaining below 1994 levels (see fig. 3). The decline coincides with the start of the changes to government policies on growth promotion and veterinarian sales profits. Danish industry and government officials noted some of the increase in antibiotic use over the last decade may be in response to disease outbreaks on swine farms. Danish government officials also mentioned, however, that the government instituted the 2010 yellow card initiative to reverse the recent increase in antibiotic use. According to these officials, antibiotic use in pig production fell 25 percent from June 2010 to June 2011 in response to the implementation of the yellow card initiative.

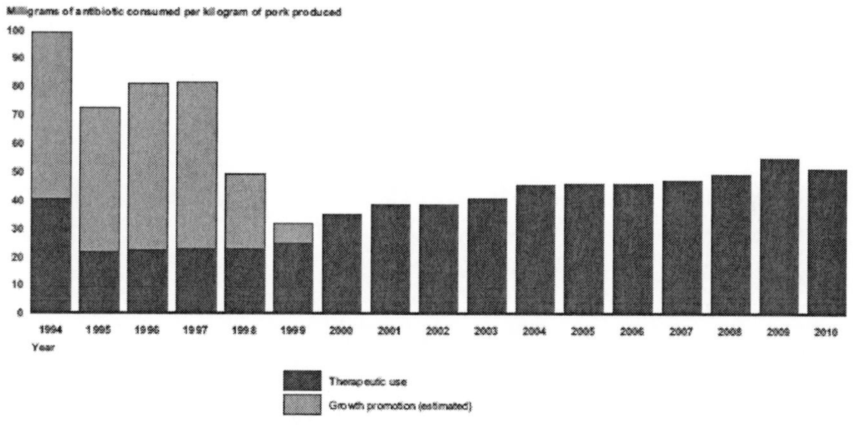

Source: DANMAP data provided by Danish officials.

Note: Between 1994 and 1999, Denmark collected data on the use of growth promotion antibiotics in aggregate, rather than by species. DANMAP officials estimated growth promotion antibiotic use in swine based on information from feed mills about the amount of feed sold and the types of growth promotion antibiotics included in the feed for the different food animal species.

Figure 3. Antibiotic Use in Swine in Denmark 1994-2010.

Denmark Resistance Data Showed Reductions in Food Animals and Retail Meat in Most Instances

According to Danish officials, Danish data on antibiotic resistance in food animals and retail meat show reductions in resistance after policy changes in most instances. Specifically, Danish government officials have tracked resistance to antibiotics banned for growth promotion among *Enterococcus* bacteria since the mid-1990s. *Enterococcus* are commonly found in the intestinal tract of humans and food animals, making them relatively easy to track over time, though they rarely cause disease.

Officials said that the percentage of *Enterococcus* from food animals that are resistant to antibiotics banned for growth promotion has decreased since the bans were implemented.

Officials also mentioned declines in resistance among Campylobacter bacteria (which can cause foodborne illness in humans) from food animals and retail meat. For example, officials said that resistance to the critically important class of drugs called macrolides has decreased in Campylobacter bacteria from swine. However, Danish industry and government officials cautioned that the association between antibiotic use and resistance is not straightforward. For example, despite restrictions on veterinary use of the critically important fluoroquinolone antibiotics since 2002, Danish resistance data have not shown a decrease in fluoroquinolone-resistant bacteria from food animals. Danish industry officials explained that restrictions on fluoroquinolone use in swine were implemented before fluoroquinolone resistance became pronounced in Denmark and that current rates of fluoroquinolone-resistant Salmonella in Danish pork are lower than for pork imported into Denmark.

Denmark Resistance Data Have Not Shown Decrease in Human Resistance, Except in Certain Instances

Danish officials told us that Denmark's resistance data have not shown a decrease in antibiotic resistance in humans after implementation of the various Danish policies, except for a few limited examples. Specifically, officials said that the prevalence of vancomycin-resistant *Enterococcus faecium* from humans has decreased since avoparcin was banned for use in animals in 1995. Resistance has been tracked for other types of bacteria and antibiotics, but similar declines have not been seen. Danish government officials explained that, in addition to antibiotic use in food animals, there are other important contributors to antibiotic resistance in humans, including human antibiotic use, consumption of imported meat (which may contain more antibiotic-resistant bacteria than Danish meat), and acquisition of resistant bacteria while traveling. Danish officials told us their data collection systems are not designed to gather information about whether human deaths from antibiotic resistance have fallen after the implementation of risk management policies. Officials mentioned a challenge to this type of data collection is that "antibiotic resistance" is not listed on death certificates as the cause of death; generally, as in the United States, the cause of death would be listed as multiple organ failure, making it difficult to identify deaths caused by antibiotic-resistant infections.

Danish Policies Do Not Appear to Have Led to an Increase in Bacteria that Cause Foodborne Illness

Denmark has also tracked the prevalence of bacteria that cause human foodborne illness on retail meat products, according to Danish industry officials. Producer organizations in the United States have expressed concerns that reductions in antibiotic use may lead to an increase in foodborne pathogens on meat, but industry officials in Denmark said that their data show no increase in the rates of these bacteria on meat products. These officials said, however, that several changes to management practices in slaughter plants may have helped ensure rates of foodborne pathogens on meat remained low. For example, these officials said Danish slaughter plants now use a flash-freezing technique—called blast chilling—that freezes the outer layer of an animal carcass, reducing the number of bacteria on the meat and even killing most Campylobacter.

Danish Policies Affected Poultry and Swine Producers Differently

Danish producers and veterinary officials noted that the policies were easier for poultry producers to implement than for swine producers. Poultry producers had made changes to their production practices throughout the 1990s to eradicate *Salmonella* from their flocks, and these practices also helped maintain flock health without routine antibiotic use. In contrast, swine producers faced difficulties weaning piglets without antibiotics, reporting both an increase in mortality and a reduction in daily weight gain shortly after the ban. However, Danish industry officials explained that swine producers implemented multiple changes to production practices that enabled them to comply with the ban. These production practices included improved genetic selection, later weaning, improved diet, increased space per piglet, and improved flooring. Industry officials explained that such changes in production practices did have real costs to the industry. For example, weaning piglets later increases the time between litters and reduces the overall number of piglets produced annually. Despite these additional costs, however, Danish industry officials expressed pride in their ability to produce high-quality meat products while ensuring that they do not contribute unduly to the problem of antibiotic resistance.

The EU Faces Challenges but Is Working to Collect Use and Resistance Data

EU officials told us that they rely on member states to collect data on antibiotic use. As of September 2010, 10 countries in Europe collected data on sales of antibiotics used in food animals, and 5 of these countries collected species-specific data.[15] In addition, 12 other countries have recently started or planned to begin collecting antibiotic sales data.[16] Among countries that currently collect use data, these data are collected using different methods, which complicates comparing them across countries. EU officials identified several challenges to collecting information about antibiotic use throughout the EU. Specifically, identifying sources of detailed information about antibiotic use is difficult because EU countries have different distribution systems for veterinary medicines and therefore collect this information in varying ways. For example, in Denmark, such data are collected from veterinary pharmacies, but not all EU countries require animal antibiotics to be dispensed through pharmacies. In addition, EU countries vary in the extent to which veterinary prescriptions are monitored electronically, making it difficult to track prescriptions consistently throughout the EU.

Despite these challenges, EU officials emphasized the importance of gathering data on antibiotic use in food animals for two reasons. First, they noted that tracking antibiotic use data allows governments to evaluate the effects of their risk management policies. Second, they mentioned that data on both antibiotic use and antibiotic resistance are needed in order to fully understand how use in animals is related to resistance in humans. Given the importance of collecting data, the EU has begun a pilot project to collect comparable antibiotic use data throughout the EU. The first phase will use a standard instrument to collect, harmonize, and analyze data on sales of veterinary antibiotics from countries that agree to participate. EU officials said that a report on sales of veterinary medicines, covering nine European countries, will be available in September 2011. EU officials said that subsequent phases will include more detailed data about species and purpose of use. They emphasized the importance of going beyond bulk sales data, noting that it is necessary to report antibiotic use in the context of the number of animals being treated or the pounds of meat produced, since it can allow for comparisons between EU countries as well as comparisons to human antibiotic use. EU officials said that the Danish system uses this type of data collection, and that WHO is working on developing guidance for how to create such data collection systems.

For resistance data, EU officials told us that the EU has been collecting information from numerous member countries and working to improve the comparability of the data between countries. In 2006, the EU produced its first report for data gathered in 2004, collating information from 26 individual countries. However, EU officials said that resistance data cannot currently be compared across countries or aggregated to provide conclusions about the entire EU, though officials are in the process of developing a report that will provide EU-wide information. Instead, officials pointed to trends identified in particular member countries. For example, officials noted a decrease in resistance in *Enterococcus* from broiler chickens after avoparcin was banned for growth promotion uses in Germany, the Netherlands, and Italy. Officials also mentioned similar declines in resistance among *Enterococcus* from healthy humans in Germany and the Netherlands.

Moreover, in addition to their data collection efforts on antibiotic use in food animals and antibiotic resistance in humans, meat, and food animals, the EU also conducts periodic baseline surveys to determine the prevalence of particular drug-resistant bacteria throughout all countries in the EU. EU officials said these baseline studies provide information that is comparable across countries. EU officials explained that EU countries are required to participate in these studies, which usually last 1 year and are used to set reduction targets for regulatory programs or to develop risk management measures. For example, in 2008 the EU conducted a prevalence study of MRSA in swine herds. It determined that the prevalence varied dramatically between member countries—it was found in more than 50 percent of swine herds in Spain, but in eight other EU countries there were no detections.

Denmark and EU Officials Emphasized Industry Role in Research

According to Danish government and industry officials we interviewed, the Danish government does not conduct research on alternatives to antibiotic use. Both industry and government officials agreed that it should be government's role to set regulatory policy and industry's role to conduct research on how to meet regulatory goals. The Danish Agriculture and Food Council—an industry organization representing producers of a variety of meat and agricultural products—has funded several studies examining alternatives to growth promotion antibiotics. For example, one such study examined the economics of five types of products that had the potential to improve feed efficiency in swine without leading to antibiotic resistance and found that few products were both economical for farmers and successful in improving feed efficiency.

EU officials also reported that at the EU-level government does not conduct a significant amount of research related to alternatives to antibiotics. They noted, however, that the EU has been trying to incentivize private industry to develop alternatives in other ways. For example, EU officials have tried to spur pharmaceutical companies to develop products to improve feed efficiency and growth by lengthening patents on such products. EU officials said that this results in a reduction in competition from generic manufacturers and has led to more than 300 applications for new feed additive products.

CONCLUSIONS

Antibiotic resistance is a growing public health problem worldwide, and any use of antibiotics—in humans or animals—can lead to the development of resistance. In 2001, USDA and HHS agencies took steps to coordinate their actions on surveillance, prevention and control of resistance, research, and product development through the 2001 interagency plan. The surveillance focus area of this plan includes action items related to improving efforts to monitor both antibiotic use in food animals, as well as antibiotic resistance in food animals and in retail meat. According to WHO, populations sampled for surveillance purposes should normally be representative of the total population—in this case, food animals and retail meat in the United States.

Since 2001, however, USDA and HHS agencies have made limited progress in improving data collection on antibiotic use and resistance. For example, although FDA has a new effort to collect data on antibiotics sold for use in food animals, these data lack crucial details, such as the species in which the antibiotics are used and the purpose for their use. The 2001 interagency plan states such data are essential for interpreting trends and variations in rates of resistance, improving the understanding of the relationship between antibiotic use and resistance, and identifying interventions to prevent and control resistance. In addition, two USDA agencies collect data on antibiotic use from food animal producers, but data from these surveys provide only a snapshot of antibiotic use practices and cannot be used to examine trends. Collecting data on antibiotic use in food animals can be challenging and costly, but without an approach to collecting more detailed data, USDA and HHS cannot track the effectiveness of policies they undertake to curb resistance. Indeed, FDA currently does not have a plan to measure the effectiveness of its voluntary strategy to reduce food animal use of antibiotics that are medically important to humans. Although there are challenges to collecting detailed data on antibiotic use, efforts are under way in the EU to begin collecting such data.

For data on antibiotic resistance, HHS and USDA agencies have leveraged existing programs to collect samples of bacteria, but the resulting data are not representative of antibiotic resistance in food animals and retail meat throughout the United States. According to the 2001 interagency plan, antibiotic resistance data will allow agencies to detect resistance trends and improve their understanding of the relationship between use and resistance. FDA is aware of the NARMS sampling limitations and has included a strategic goal of making NARMS sampling more representative and applicable to trend analysis in its draft 2011-2015 NARMS Strategic Plan. FDA officials mentioned several ways that NARMS sampling could be improved, such as discontinuing slaughter plant sampling in favor of an on-farm sampling program and increasing the number of states participating in the retail meat program.

USDA and HHS have also undertaken some research related to developing alternatives to current antibiotic use practices. However, the extent of these research efforts is unclear, as neither USDA nor HHS has assessed its research efforts to determine the progress made toward the related action item in the 2001 interagency plan. In addition, officials from most of the veterinary and several public health organizations we spoke with said that the federal government should make greater efforts to coordinate this research with the food animal industry. Without an assessment of past research efforts and coordination with industry, USDA and HHS may be limited in their ability to identify gaps where additional research is needed. In addition, USDA and HHS managers may not have the critical information they need to make decisions about future research efforts. Focus on tracking progress and making sound decisions about future research is particularly important in light of the fiscal pressures currently facing the federal government. Nevertheless, the draft 2010 interagency plan includes an action item on researching alternatives, but it does not identify steps the agencies intend to take to do so. Similarly, USDA and HHS had sought to educate producers and veterinarians about appropriate antibiotic use but did not assess their efforts. The one remaining education activity, however, is a $70,400 USDA training module on antibiotic resistance for veterinarians, which will be completed in 2012, after which there are no plans to develop new education activities.

Recommendations for Executive Action

We are making the following three recommendations:

- To track the effectiveness of policies to curb antibiotic resistance, including FDA's voluntary strategy designed to reduce antibiotic use in food animals and to address action items in the surveillance focus area of the 2001 interagency plan, we recommend the Secretaries of Agriculture and Health and Human Services direct agencies to, consistent with their existing authorities, (1) identify potential approaches for collecting detailed data on antibiotic use in food animals, including the species in which antibiotics are used and the purpose for their use, as well as the costs, time frames, and potential trade-offs associated with each approach; (2) collaborate with industry to select the best approach; (3) seek any resources necessary to implement the approach; and (4) use the data to assess the effectiveness of policies to curb antibiotic resistance.

- To enhance surveillance of antibiotic-resistant bacteria in food animals, we recommend that the Secretaries of Agriculture and Health and Human Services direct agencies to, consistent with their existing authorities, modify NARMS sampling to make the data more representative of antibiotic resistance in food animals and retail meat throughout the United States.
- To better focus future federal research efforts on alternatives to current antibiotic use practices, we recommend that the Secretaries of Agriculture and Health and Human Services direct agencies to (1) assess previous research efforts on alternatives and identify gaps where additional research is needed, in collaboration with the animal production industry, and (2) specify steps in the draft 2010 interagency plan that agencies will take to fill those gaps.

AGENCY COMMENTS AND OUR EVALUATION

We provided the Departments of Agriculture and Health and Human Services a draft of this report for review and comment. Both departments agreed with our recommendations and provided written comments on the draft, which are summarized below and appear in their entirety in appendixes VII and VIII, respectively, of this report. The departments also provided technical comments, which we incorporated as appropriate.

In its comments, USDA agreed with our recommendations. In response to our recommendation on collecting antibiotic use data, USDA noted that the department has devised strategies to collect detailed information on antibiotic use in food animals, as documented in “A USDA Plan to Address Antimicrobial Resistance.” Our report discusses many of the ongoing USDA activities described in the document, including NAHMS, ARMS, and NARMS. In commenting on our recommendation to collect more representative resistance data, USDA acknowledged that sampling for antibiotic resistant bacteria in food animals is not currently conducted on a nationally representative population, but also stated that NARMS data can still be used to examine general trends. We continue to believe that the nonrandom sampling method used for food animals in NARMS results in data that are not representative of food animals across the country and cannot be used for trend analysis. Moreover, as our report states, the NARMS program has prioritized modifying animal sampling to overcome its current biases, and both FDA and USDA have identified efforts that could be used to improve NARMS food animal sampling. In its letter, USDA identified several such efforts; we had included several of these in the draft report, and we modified the final version to include the remaining effort.

In its comments, HHS also agreed with our recommendations, but stated that FDA has made substantial progress and taken an active and deliberative role in addressing the controversial and complex issue of antibiotic use in food animals. We acknowledge that FDA has taken many actions, most of which are discussed in the report. However, as our report states, since the 2001 interagency plan, USDA and HHS agencies have made limited progress in improving data collection on antibiotic use and resistance. Specifically, as we noted in our report, FDA's data on sales of antibiotics for animal use do not include information on the species in which antibiotics are used or the purpose for their use, which, for example, prevents agencies from interpreting trends and variations in rates of resistance. Similarly, as our report states, data on antibiotic resistance from food animals are not representative and cannot be used for trend analysis—even though the 2001 interagency plan identified detecting resistance trends as an important part of monitoring for antibiotic resistance. In commenting on our recommendation regarding antibiotic use data collection, FDA recognized that having more detailed antibiotic use data would benefit its overall effort to assure the judicious use of antibiotics. FDA also noted that it is exploring potential approaches for obtaining more detailed information and that it plans to coordinate with USDA in that effort. We modified our report to include this information. In addition, regarding our findings on FDA's resistance data from retail meat, FDA stated that it does not believe samples need to be statistically representative of the entire United States to serve as indicators of U.S. retail meat. We modified our report to better reflect FDA's position, but as our report states, the FDA Science Advisory Board's 2007 review of data on antibiotic resistance in retail meat found that the lack of a national sampling strategy limits a broader interpretation of NARMS data.

Sincerely yours,
Lisa Shames
Director,
Natural Resources and Environment

APPENDIX I: OBJECTIVES, SCOPE, AND METHODOLOGY

The objectives of our review were to determine (1) the extent to which federal agencies have collected data on antibiotic use and resistance in food animals; (2) the actions the Food and Drug Administration (FDA) has taken to mitigate the risk of antibiotic resistance in humans as a result of antibiotic use in food animals; (3) the extent to which federal agencies have conducted research on alternatives to current antibiotic use practices and educated producers and veterinarians about appropriate antibiotic use; and (4) what actions the European Union (EU) and an EU member country, Denmark, have taken to regulate antibiotic use in food animals and what lessons, if any, have been learned.

To address the first three objectives of our study, we reviewed federal laws, regulations, policies, and guidance; federal plans about antibiotic resistance; agency documents related to data collection efforts on antibiotic use and resistance; and documents from international organizations and other countries related to surveillance of animal antibiotic use and resistance. In particular, we reviewed the Food, Conservation, and Energy Act of 2008 (2008 Farm Bill), as well as laws related to FDA's oversight of animal antibiotics, including the Federal Food, Drug, and Cosmetic Act, the Animal Drug Availability Act of 1996, the Animal Drug User Fee Act of 2003. We also reviewed regulations and guidance implementing FDA's authorities, including *Evaluating the Safety of Antimicrobial New Animal Drugs with Regard to Their Microbiological Effects on Bacteria of Human Health Concern* (Guidance for Industry #152), and *The Judicious Use of Medically Important Antimicrobial Drugs in Food-Producing Animals* (draft Guidance for Industry #209). In addition, we reviewed the 2001 Interagency Public Health Action Plan to Combat Antimicrobial Resistance, the draft 2010 Interagency Public Health Action Plan to Combat Antimicrobial Resistance, and agencies' annual updates of activities they completed related to these plans. We also reviewed agency documents related to FDA's sales data, the National Animal Health Monitoring System (NAHMS), the Agricultural Resource Management Survey (ARMS), the National Antimicrobial Resistance Monitoring System (NARMS), and the now-defunct pilot Collaboration on Animal Health and Food Safety Epidemiology (CAHFSE). Internationally, we reviewed documents from surveillance systems in Canada and Denmark, including reports about the Canadian Integrated Program on Antimicrobial Resistance Surveillance (CIPARS) and the Danish Antimicrobial Resistance Monitoring and Research Programme (DANMAP). In addition, we reviewed the World Health Organization's guidance on developing surveillance systems for antibiotic resistance related to food animal antibiotic use.

To discuss topics related to the first three objectives, we also conducted interviews with officials at the Department of Health and Human Services' (HHS) Centers for Disease Control and Prevention (CDC), FDA, and the National Institutes of Health (NIH) and U.S. Department of Agriculture (USDA) agency officials at the Animal and Plant Health Inspection Service (APHIS), the Agricultural Research Service (ARS), the Economic Research Service (ERS), the Food Safety and Inspection Service (FSIS), and the National Institute of Food and Agriculture (NIFA). We also interviewed an official representing CIPARS to discuss the program's efforts to monitor antibiotic use and resistance in animals across Canada, the challenges it faces, and how the program may relate to current and future data collection efforts in the United States.

We also conducted site visits with conventional and alternative (either organic or antibiotic-free) producers of poultry, cattle, swine, and dairy products in Delaware, Georgia, Iowa, Kansas, Minnesota, and Wisconsin to obtain a better understanding of production practices and the types of antibiotic use data available at the farm level. During these site visits, we spoke with producers, veterinarians, academic researchers, and extension agents involved with food animal production. We selected these commodity groups because they represent the top four animal products in the United States. We selected our site visit locations based on the accessibility of production facilities of different sizes—we visited both small and large facilities; including states that are among the largest producers of each commodity in our scope of study; and proximity to Washington, D.C., and the USDA NARMS laboratory in Georgia. These sites were selected using a nonprobability sample and the findings from those visits cannot be generalized to other producers.

Based on issues identified by reviewing documents and interviewing federal, state, and local officials, we developed a questionnaire on the use of antibiotics in animals and resistance. The questionnaire gathered organizations' perspectives on a range of topics including the extent to which federal data collection programs support the action items identified by federal agencies in the 2001 interagency plan; what actions, if any, FDA or other federal agencies should take to implement the two principles FDA outlined in draft Guidance for Industry #209 and how such implementation may affect antibiotic use in food animals; and what role, if any, the federal government should have in conducting research on alternatives to current antibiotic use practices and educating producers and veterinarians. We conducted a pretest of the questionnaire and made appropriate changes based on the pretest.

In addition to developing the questionnaire, we identified 11 organizations involved with the issue of antibiotic use in food animals and antibiotic resistance. We selected these organizations because of their expertise in topics surrounding antibiotic use in animals and resistance based on whether they have been actively involved in this issue within the past 5 years, including through testimonies to Congress, in-depth public discussions, or published research; and to provide representation across producer organizations that represent the major commodities, in addition to pharmaceutical and public health organizations. The selected organizations are a nonprobability sample, and their responses are not generalizable. The selected organizations were: National Cattleman's Beef Association, National Milk Producers' Federation, National Pork Producers Council, National Chicken Council, Animal Health Institute, Alliance for the Prudent Use of Antibiotics, Center for Science in the Public Interest, Infectious Diseases Society of America, Keep Antibiotics Working, PEW Campaign on Human Health and Industrial Farming, and Union of Concerned Scientists.

We administered the questionnaires through structured interviews with representatives from the 11 national organizations, who spoke on behalf of their members, either via phone or in-person. All 11 organizations agreed to participate in these structured interviews. To identify trends in responses, we qualitatively analyzed the open-ended responses from the interviews to provide insight into organizations' views on the issues identified in the questionnaire.

We also conducted structured interviews with representatives from five national veterinary organizations, who spoke on behalf of their members, to discuss their views on federal research efforts on alternatives and federal efforts to educate producers and veterinarians about appropriate use. The questionnaire covered a range of topics including federal progress in both of these areas since 2001 and actions the federal government can take to improve future efforts in these areas. We contacted five veterinary organizations to request their participation, selecting these organizations to include the largest U.S. veterinary organization—the American Veterinary Medical Association—as well as a veterinary organization representing each of the major commodities in our review—American Association of Avian Pathologists, American Association of Bovine Practitioners, American Association of Swine Veterinarians, and the Academy of Veterinary Consultants. We distributed the questionnaire to the five organizations electronically and administered the questionnaires through structured interviews with each organization via phone or in person. All five veterinary organizations agreed to participate in these structured interviews. To identify trends in responses, we qualitatively analyzed the open-ended responses from the interviews to provide insight into organizations' views on the issues identified in the questionnaire. Although we sought to include a variety of organizations with perspectives about antibiotic use and resistance, the views of organizations consulted should not be considered to represent all perspectives about these issues and are not generalizable.

To describe actions the EU and Denmark have taken to regulate antibiotic use in food animals and potential lessons that have been learned from these actions, we reviewed documents, spoke with EU and Danish government and industry officials, and visited producers. We selected the EU and Denmark because they implemented bans on growth promotion uses of antibiotics in 2006 and 2000, respectively, which allows for a review of the effects of these policies in the years since. In addition, Denmark's experience with regulating antibiotic use has been well-documented in government-collected data that provide insight into the effects of policy changes.

For the EU, we reviewed documents describing EU Commission directives and regulations regarding antibiotic use in food animals, risk assessments related to antibiotic use in food animals, surveillance reports describing antibiotic resistance in the EU, and proposals for future data collection efforts on antibiotic use. In addition, we spoke with officials from the EU Directorates General for Health and Consumers, Agriculture and Rural Development, and Research and Innovation. We also spoke with an official from the European Food Safety Agency regarding their surveillance reports describing antibiotic resistance in the EU. Finally, we interviewed the following organizations that interact with the EU on behalf of their members regarding animal antibiotic use: Federation of Veterinarians of Europe, which represents veterinarians throughout the EU, and the International Federation for Animal Health, which represents pharmaceutical companies who manufacture animal health products. We did not independently verify statements of EU law.

For Denmark, we reviewed documents describing Danish laws and regulations regarding animal antibiotic use and government regulation of veterinarians, surveillance reports describing antibiotic use and antibiotic resistance in Denmark, and published studies examining Denmark's experience with regulating antibiotic use. In addition, we spoke with officials at the Danish Veterinary and Food Administration and DANMAP. We also spoke with officials at the Danish Agriculture and Food Council, which represents producers in Denmark, to learn about how Danish policies have affected producers. Finally, we conducted site visits and interviewed Danish producers and veterinarians at a poultry and a swine facility in Denmark to learn about current methods of production and how these producers have implemented Danish policies. These sites were selected based on convenience and the findings from those visits cannot be generalized to other producers. We did not independently verify statements of Danish law.

We conducted this performance audit from August 2010 to September 2011, in accordance with generally accepted government auditing standards. Those standards require that we plan and perform the audit to obtain sufficient, appropriate evidence to provide a reasonable basis for our findings and conclusions based on our audit objectives. We believe that the evidence obtained provides a reasonable basis for our findings and conclusions based on our audit objectives.

APPENDIX II: ALTERNATIVE MODES OF FOOD ANIMAL PRODUCTION

Some producers raise animals using alternative modes of production.[1] One such alternative is organic production, for which USDA's National Organic Program (NOP) develops, implements, and administers national standards. To comply with NOP standards, organically produced animals cannot be treated with antibiotics. According to USDA, organic farming has become one of the fastest-growing segments of U.S. agriculture, and consumer demand for organically produced goods has shown double-digit growth for well over a decade, providing market incentives for U.S. farmers across a broad range of commodities. According to recent industry statistics, organic sales account for over 3 percent of total U.S. food sales. Fruits and vegetables account for about 37 percent of U.S. organic food sales, while dairy and food animals (including meat, fish, and poultry) account for about 16 and 3 percent, respectively, of U.S. organic food sales.

According to the Organic Trade Association, transitioning from conventional to organic production can take several years, because producers must adopt certain management practices to qualify for organic certification. The NOP standards apply to animals used for meat, milk, eggs, and other animal products represented as organically produced. Some of the NOP livestock standards include the following:

- Animals for slaughter must be raised under organic management from the last third of gestation, or no later than the second day of life for poultry.
- Producers generally must provide a total feed ration composed of agricultural products, but they may also provide allowed vitamin and mineral supplements.
- Traditional livestock have transition periods for converting to organic. For example, producers may convert an entire distinct dairy herd to organic production by providing 80 percent organically produced feed for 9 months, followed by 3 months of 100 percent organically produced feed. If the farm did not convert an entire distinct herd, new animals added must be raised using organic methods for at least 1 year before the milk can be sold as organic.
- Organically raised animals may not be given hormones to promote growth, or antibiotics for any reason.
- All organically raised animals must have access to the outdoors, including access to pasture for ruminants, such as cattle. They may be temporarily confined only for specified reasons, including reasons of health, safety, the animal's stage of production, or to protect soil or water quality.
- A USDA-approved certifier ensures that organic producers are following all of the rules necessary to meet NOP standards, which includes maintaining data that preserve the identity of all organically managed animals and edible and nonedible animal products produced on the operation.

One producer we visited told us that his farm began the transition from a conventional farm in 1995 and became a grass-fed beef and certified organic farm in 2006 (see fig. 4). This producer also said that the transition experience was economically challenging. Specifically, during this conversion the farm stopped bringing in outside animals and changed confinement and feed practices. Through such changes, this producer said that, overall, the animals are healthier and the farm has increased marketing opportunities, which he feels outweighs the costs.

Source: GAO.

Figure 4. Grass-Fed Cattle Raised without Antibiotics.

In addition to organic, there are other alternative modes of production. For example, FSIS has a “raised without antibiotics” production label for red meat and poultry. Before FSIS will approve such a label, producers must provide the agency with sufficient documentation that demonstrates animals were raised without antibiotics. Other commonly approved FSIS poultry and meat production labels include “natural” and “free range,” though these labels do not limit the use of antibiotics (see fig. 5).

Some conventional and alternative producers we visited told us that animals produced without antibiotics typically grow at slower rates and tend to weigh less at market, requiring producers to charge higher premiums to cover these additional production costs.

Source: GAO.

Figure 5. Free-Range Chickens at a Portable Chicken House.

Producers raising animals without antibiotics typically have to take greater preventative measures, such as changes in husbandry practices, in order to reduce chances of illness. These changes in husbandry practices may include providing hay bedding for newly birthed calves and mother cows, selecting and breeding animals with disease resistance, and allowing greater access outdoors and space per animal. When animals do become sick, alternative disease treatments depend on the animal and illness. For example, cows may be treated with sea salt and a patch for pink eye and splints for broken legs. Still, antibiotics may need to be used as a last resort and, in such cases, these animals are sold to the conventional market, creating an economic loss for the producer.

APPENDIX III: THE FOOD AND DRUG ADMINISTRATION'S ANTIBIOTIC SALES DATA

Tables 7 and 8 provide examples of the data collected by the Food and Drug Administration as required by the Animal Drug User Fee Amendments of 2008 (ADUFA).

Table 7. 2009 Sales and Distribution Data, by Drug Class, for Antimicrobial Drugs Approved for Use in Food-Producing Animals in the United States

Antimicrobial class	Annual totals (kilograms of active ingredient)
Aminoglycosides	339,678
Cephalosporins	41,328
Ionophores	3,740,627
Lincosamides	115,837
Macrolides	861,985
Penicillins	610,514
Sulfas	517,873
Tetracyclines	4,611,892
Fluoroquinolones and Diaminopyrimidines combined	11,101
Aminocoumarins, Glycolipids, Quinoxalines combined	802,388
Amphenicols, Pleuromutilins, Polypeptides, and Streptogramins combined	1,413,877

Source: GAO analysis of FDA data.

Table 8. 2009 Sales and Distribution Data, by Route of Administration, for Antimicrobial Drugs Approved for Use in Food-Producing Animals in the United States

Method of administration	Amount of antimicrobial (kilograms)
In feed	9,701,180
In water	2,065,433
By injection	422,818

Source: FDA.

APPENDIX IV: STRUCTURE OF DANMAP

The objectives of the Danish Integrated Antimicrobial Resistance Monitoring and Research Program (DANMAP) are to monitor the consumption of antibiotics for food animals and humans; monitor the occurrence of antibiotic resistance in bacteria from food animals, food of animal origin, and humans; study associations between antibiotic use and resistance; and identify routes of transmission and areas for further research studies.

Table 9 shows the types of data gathered about antibiotic use and resistance in Denmark and the sources of these data.

Table 9. Components of DANMAP

Antibiotic use data		
Program component	Source of data	Type of information recorded
Animal antibiotic use (VetStat)	Prescription records from veterinary pharmacies, feed mills, veterinarians, and private companies	Farm identification number Prescribing veterinarian identification number Intended species and age group Disease being treated Medicine being prescribed Dose of medicine Date and place prescription was filled (pharmacy, feed mill, veterinarian)
Human antibiotic use (Danish Medicines Agency)	Human pharmacies (including hospital pharmacies)	Identification number of patient Identification number of prescribing physician Date and place prescription was filled (i.e., pharmacy, hospital pharmacy) Payment/reimbursement method Medicine being prescribed Dose of medicine
Antibiotic resistance data		
Entity under surveillance	Source of bacteria samples	Bacteria tested for resistance
Animals	Healthy production animals at slaughter plants	Escherischia coli Enterococcus faecium Enterococcus faecalis Campylobacter coli Campylobacter jejuni

Table 9. (Continued)

Antibiotic resistance data		
Entity under surveillance	Source of bacteria samples	Bacteria tested for resistance
Animals (*continued*)	Diagnostic laboratory submissions	E. coli O149 and E. coli F5 (K99)
	Danish Salmonella surveillance program in swine and broiler chickens	Salmonella
	Clinical and subclinical infections	Salmonella Typhimurium
Food	Wholesale and retail food samples from both Danish and imported foods	Campylobacter indicator E. coli
	Danish Salmonella surveillance program in pork and beef; risk-based Salmonella surveillance program for Danish poultry and imported meat	Enterococci Salmonella
Humans[a]	A proportion of patients diagnosed with Salmonella or Campylobacter infections	Salmonella enterica serovars Typhimurium and Enteritidis Campylobacter jejuni

Antibiotic resistance data		
Entity under surveillance	Source of bacteria samples	Bacteria tested for resistance
Humans[a] *(continued)*	Blood samples of Staphylococcus aureus are sent to the Statens Serum Institute on a voluntary basis; it is mandatory to submit samples of all methicillin-resistant Staphylococcus aureus (MRSA)	Staphylococcus aureus
	All blood and spinal fluid samples are sent to the Statens Serum Institute	Invasive Streptococcus pneumoniae, Streptococcus pyogenes (group A streptococci), group B, C, and G streptococci
	All blood and spinal fluid samples are sent to the Statens Serum Institute	Invasive Streptococcus pneumoniae, Streptococcus pyogenes (group A streptococci), group B, C, and G streptococci
	All samples from blood, urine, or other samples were submitted to the Statens Serum Institute	Escherichia coli Klebsiella pneumoniae Pseudomonas aeruginosa noninvasive Streptococcus pneumoniae noninvasive Streptococcus pyogenes invasive E. faecium invasive E. faecalis

Source: DANMAP.

[a] Some DANMAP reports include analysis of bacterial samples taken from healthy humans. However, DANMAP 2009 did not.

Appendix V: ARS and NIFA Research Activities Related to Alternatives to Current Antibiotic Use Practices

Agency	Grantee(s) (if applicable)	Project title	Project year(s)	Description	Total funding
ARS	University of Arkansas	Development of Nonantibiotic Alternatives for Foodborne Pathogen Control in Turkeys	2001-2006	Studied effectiveness of nonantibiotic drug therapies (specifically bacteriophages) in eliminating certain bacteria in poultry	Not provided by the agency
	Not applicable	Characterization and Enhancement of Immune Responses of Calves	2002-2006; 2006-2011	Studied the immune systems of calves and sought to construct an oral vaccine and devise nutrition-based approaches that promote disease resistance	$443,500 (FY 2010)[a, b]
	Not applicable	Development of Alternative Approaches to Antibiotics for Controlling Bacterial Respiratory Pathogens in Poultry	2002-2006; 2007-2012	Studying the effectiveness of nonantibiotic drug therapies (specifically bacteriophages) at preventing and treating specific diseases in poultry	Not provided by the agency[a]
	Not applicable	Interventions to Reduce Epizootic Pathogenic Bacteria in Swine and Cattle	2005-2010	Researched management strategies that may help reduce foodborne bacteria in swine and cattle	Not provided by the agency[a]
	Not applicable	Impact of Diet and Gut Microbial Ecology on Foodborne Bacterial Pathogens and Antimicrobial Resistance in Farm Animals	2005-2010	Studied genes resistant to certain bacteria in food animals and dietary strategies to limit certain diseases in food animals	$373,800 (FY 2010)[a, b]
	Not applicable	Interventions and Methodologies to Reduce Human and Foodborne Bacterial Pathogens in Chickens	2005-2010	Researched the effectiveness of methodologies such as nonantibiotic drug therapies (specifically peptides and bacteriophages) and certain management practices in reducing or eliminating specific bacteria in poultry farms	Not provided by the agency[a]

Agency	Grantee(s) (if applicable)	Project title	Project year(s)	Description	Total funding
NIFA[c]	Michigan State University	Neutrophil Apoptosis Delay at Parturition-Mechanisms and Inflammatory Consequences During Interaction with Mastitis-Causing Coliforms	2006-2010	Researched nonantibiotic drug therapies (specifically novel blood factors and neutrophil behaviors) to prevent or treat mastitis in calves	$348,000
	University of California; Washington State University	Dissemination of Cephalosporin Resistance Genes	2005-2008; 2007-2008	Studied the relationship between therapeutic antibiotic use and antibiotic resistance in animals	$980,000; $425,434
	University of California; Washington State University	Reducing the Use of Antibiotics and the Incidence of Antibiotic Resistance on Calf Ranches	2004-2007; 2007-2009	Evaluated the effectiveness of three management strategies that may reduce the use of antibiotics and the incidence of antibiotic resistance in calf rearing facilities	$600,000; $245,204
	Iowa State University	Functional Genomics and Cellular Immunity to Salmonella	2007-2011	Researched nonantibiotic therapeutic strategies to reduce bacterial burden in poultry, in order to improve production and food safety	$472,356
	Oklahoma State University	Enhancing Disease Resistance by Boosting Innate Immunity	2008-2011	Researched the effectiveness of nonantibiotic drug therapies (specifically peptides) in disease control and prevention for food animals, while minimizing the use of antibiotics and emergence of drug-resistant pathogens	$365,500
	Ohio State University	The Relationship Between Poultry Litter and the Intestinal Microbial Community Profile in Broilers	2008-2012	Studying the presence of bacteria populations over time under varying management strategies	$308,086
	ARS	Engineering Bacteriophage Endolysins: Antimicrobials for Mastitis Pathogens That are Refractory to Resistance Development	2007-2011	Explored the development of a new antibiotic that may be used to treat mastitis without causing resistance development	$348,703

Appendix V. (Continued)

Agency	Grantee(s) (if applicable)	Project title	Project year(s)	Description	Total funding
	Ohio State University	Combating the Transmission of Antibiotic Resistance through the Global Food Chain	2008-2011	Researched methods to minimize antibiotic resistance transmission through the global food chain, improve safety of global food supplies, and enhance U.S. leadership in the global market	$99,979
	North Carolina State University	Molecular Epidemiology of Salmonella in Conventional and Antimicrobial Free Swine Production Systems	2008-2011	Studied the makeup and presence of Salmonella over time in conventional verses antibiotic-free production systems	$389,383
	Texas A&M University	Novel Pre-Harvest Interventions to Protect Antimicrobials of Critical Importance in Human and Veterinary Medicine	2008-2012	Evaluating potential interventions that may manage antibiotic-resistant bacteria in animal agriculture	$939,999
	University of Connecticut	Investigating the Potential of Natural Antimicrobials for Controlling Bovine Mastitis	2009-2011	Studied the development of new antibiotics to control mastitis which could help decrease use of antibiotics in bovine operations and decrease antibiotic-resistant bacteria in milk	$150,000
	Ohio State University	Effectiveness of Reduced Agricultural Antimicrobial Usage as a Food Safety Intervention	2010-2013	Studying the effects of antibiotic use on bacteria emergence and on antibiotic resistance	$399,924
	Kansas State University	Practical Interventions to Effectively Manage Antibiotic Resistance in Beef and Dairy Cattle Systems: A Fully Integrated Approach	2010-2014	Identifying, evaluating, and implementing interventions for managing antibiotic resistance in beef and dairy cattle systems	$2,000,000
	Washington State University	Minimizing Antibiotic Resistance Transmission: The Dairy Farm as a Model System	2010-2014	Researching methods and strategies to reduce antibiotic resistance transmission along the food chain	$2,000,000

Source: GAO analysis of agency documents.

[a] The focus of this project was not specifically on the development of alternatives to antibiotic use but has provided a framework for future research efforts focused on the impact of alternatives.

[b] This figure is based on fiscal year 2010 funding levels, and is similar to funding for each year of the project.

[c] In 2010, NIFA was allocated up to $4 million to award two competitive grants related to antibiotic resistance and use (awarded to Kansas State University and Washington State University). NIFA expects to make decisions about similar grants for fiscal year 2011 in September, and to release award announcements in fiscal year 2012.

APPENDIX VI: CDC AND FDA RESEARCH ACTIVITIES RELATED TO ALTERNATIVES TO CURRENT ANTIBIOTIC USE PRACTICES

Agencies	Grantees	Project title	Project years	Description	Total funding
CDC, FDA	University of Georgia, North Carolina State University, Colorado State University, Washington State University	Reducing Resistant Bacteria in Food Animals	2001-2003	Two studies in dairy cattle and two in swine to assess the impact of antibiotic use, develop alternatives to the use of antibiotics as growth promotants, and to evaluate new practices that reduce resistant bacteria in food animals	Not provided by the agency
	Not provided by the agency	Get Smart on the Farm: Reducing Resistant Bacteria in Food Animals	2004-2005	Studies to understand and look at ways to reduce resistance in food animals and to investigate alternative therapies to antibiotics	Not provided by the agency[a]

Source: GAO analysis of agency documents.

[a] Funding for this research activity came from the total $1,716,600 used to fund all of the Get Smart on the Farm related activities from 2003-2010. Officials were unable to provide detailed funding amount for this specific research activity.

APPENDIX VII: COMMENTS FROM THE DEPARTMENT OF AGRICULTURE

United States Department of Agriculture

Office of the Secretary
Washington, D.C. 20250

AUG 25 2011

Ms. Lisa Shames, Director
Natural Resources and Environment
United States Government Accountability Office
441 G Street, NW
Washington, DC 20548

Dear Ms. Shames:

The United States Department of Agriculture (USDA) has reviewed the U.S. Government Accountability Office's (GAO) Draft Report, "Antibiotic Resistance: Agencies Have Made Limited Progress Addressing Antibiotic Use in Animals" (11-801). While USDA agrees with each Recommendation, we offer the following perspectives on each Recommendation.

Overall, USDA believes that actions taken to address antimicrobial resistance should be based on science. Currently, there is insufficient scientific information available to make important policy decisions regarding use of antibiotics for growth promotion purposes. Such policy decisions may, in some cases as described in the GAO report, actually lead to increased use of antibiotics with unknown potential effects on overall antibiotic resistance and public health. GAO's assessment that the National Antimicrobial Resistance Monitoring System (NARMS) data cannot be used to assess antibiotic resistance trends on livestock and poultry operations is not entirely accurate. While these data do not provide a national estimate of antibiotic resistance in animal agriculture and are collected on a rotational basis, the methods used for collection of these data are consistent across studies and can be used to examine general trends.

GAO Recommendation

To track the effectiveness of policies to curb antibiotic resistance, including FDA's voluntary strategy designed to reduce antibiotic use in food animals and to address action items in the surveillance focus area of the 2001 interagency plan, GAO recommends the Secretaries of Agriculture and Health and Human Services direct agencies to, consistent with their existing authorities, 1) identify potential approaches for collecting detailed data on antibiotic use in food animals, including the species in which antibiotics are used and the purpose for their use, as well as the costs, time frames, and potential tradeoffs associated with each approach; 2) collaborate with industry to select the best approach; 3) seek any resources necessary to implement the approach; and 4) use the data to assess the effectiveness of policies to curb antibiotic resistance.

An Equal Opportunity Employer

Ms. Lisa Shames
Page 2

USDA Response

USDA agrees with this Recommendation. USDA has proactively devised strategies to identify approaches to more effectively collect detailed information on antibiotic use in food animals, as documented in the report titled "A USDA Plan to Address Antimicrobial Resistance," dated September 3, 2010. This report described a portfolio of current and planned activities with anticipated funding at current levels and additional recommended activities that would require additional funding. This portfolio of activities represented a broad USDA-wide approach incorporating actions in many different agencies. Under ideal circumstances, USDA would engage the industry in identifying the optimal mix of activities to garner the data needed to meet part 4 of this Recommendation. Our Agricultural Research Service (ARS), in conjunction with the Food and Drug Administration (FDA), is piloting two different approaches on collecting antibiotic use data in food animals and potential tradeoffs for each approach. This is being done in collaboration with experts from industry, government, and academia. USDA is committed to working collaboratively with stakeholders including industry and other government entities to use the data to craft science-based policy to mitigate risks where appropriate.

GAO Recommendation

To enhance surveillance of antibiotic-resistant bacteria in food animals, GAO recommends the Secretaries of Agriculture and Health and Human Services direct agencies to, consistent with their existing authorities, modify NARMS sampling to make the data more representative of antibiotic resistance in food animals and retail meat throughout the United States.

USDA Response

USDA agrees with this Recommendation. The NARMS sampling is not currently conducted on a randomly-selected, nationally-representative population of food animals and retail meat in the U.S. In consultation with its Federal partners, our Food Safety and Inspection Service (FSIS) is evaluating options for changing its *Salmonella* verification program to provide sampling data to NARMS that will allow for more representative characterization of antibiotic resistance in food animals and retail meat and poultry. Budget constraints and FSIS food safety verification program needs significantly influence this evaluation. The Animal and Plant Health Inspection Service (APHIS) continues to evaluate options to determine the prevalence of resistance and frequency and manner of use of antibiotics in the pre-harvest animal production environments. ARS is working with FDA to develop several approaches to enhance the accuracy and monitoring of the animal sampling collected for NARMS. These strategies will be evaluated to determine the best approach for future revisions to NARMS. Changes to the

Ms. Lisa Shames
Page 3

NARMS program will be done in cooperation with NARMS' collaborating agencies, which include USDA's APHIS and FSIS, and HHS' FDA, and Centers for Disease Control and Prevention (CDC).

GAO Recommendation

To better focus future federal research efforts on alternatives to current antibiotic use practices, we recommend that the Secretaries of Agriculture and Health and Human Services direct agencies to 1) assess previous research efforts on alternatives and identify gaps where additional research is needed, in collaboration with the animal production industry, and 2) specify steps in the draft 2010 interagency plan that agencies will take to fill those gaps.

USDA Response

USDA agrees with this Recommendation. The 2011 interagency plan can be improved to better outline potential actions for research alternatives to antibiotics. Assessment in this area has not been done because the outcome measurements have not been defined. Actual alternative products must be approved by FDA. Other alternatives such as vaccines or management practices are evaluated by disease prevention rather than as a specific product and as stated earlier are impossible to measure in the context of reduced antibiotic use. Some milestones that ARS has used previously are number of peer-reviewed publications, technology transfers, and patents.

Sincerely,

Edward Avalos
Under Secretary
Marketing and Regulatory Programs

APPENDIX VIII: COMMENTS FROM THE DEPARTMENT OF HEALTH AND HUMAN SERVICES

DEPARTMENT OF HEALTH & HUMAN SERVICES OFFICE OF THE SECRETARY

Assistant Secretary for Legislation
Washington, DC 20201

AUG 15 2011

Lisa Shames
Director, Natural Resources and Environment
U.S. Government Accountability Office
441 G Street N.W.
Washington, DC 20548

Dear Ms. Shames:

Attached are comments on the U.S. Government Accountability Office's (GAO) draft report entitled: "ANTIBIOTIC RESISTANCE: Agencies Have Made Limited Progress Addressing Antibiotic Use In Animals" (GAO-11-801).

The Department appreciates the opportunity to review this report before its publication.

Sincerely,

Jim R. Esquea
Assistant Secretary for Legislation

Attachment

GENERAL COMMENTS OF THE DEPARTMENT OF HEALTH AND HUMAN SERVICES (HHS) ON THE GOVERNMENT ACCOUNTABILITY OFFICE'S (GAO) DRAFT REPORT ENTITLED, "ANTIBIOTIC RESISTANCE: AGENCIES HAVE MADE LIMITED PROGRESS ADDRESSING ANTIBIOTIC USE IN ANIMALS" (GAO-11-801)

The Department appreciates the opportunity to review and comment on this draft report. While the Food and Drug Administration (FDA) generally agrees with GAO's recommendations, FDA has made substantial progress and has taken an active and deliberative role in addressing the complex and controversial issue of antibiotic use in food-producing animals. FDA's work in this area is ongoing, and includes a number of important accomplishments, including several initiatives that are relevant to GAO's recommendations. Some of the important steps that have been taken to date include the following:

- In 1996, the National Antimicrobial Resistance Monitoring System (NARMS) was established. NARMS provides ongoing monitoring data on antimicrobial resistance patterns in select zoonotic foodborne bacteria. NARMS surveillance and research activities are designed to supply the data needed to inform and prioritize science-based approaches to assuring food safety, and to reduce uncertainty about the potential public health risks posed by antimicrobial use in food animals. FDA's Center for Veterinary Medicine (CVM) is the lead coordinator of NARMS and collaborates with the Centers for Disease Control and Prevention (CDC), the U.S. Department of Agriculture's Agricultural Research Service (ARS), and state public health laboratories to collect data to monitor antimicrobial resistant foodborne pathogens in animal carcasses at slaughter, in retail meats, and in human clinical cases.

- In 1999, FDA published a "Framework Document" and convened public meetings to gather public input on developing an approach for evaluating antimicrobial resistance safety concerns as part of the new animal drug approval process.

- In 2001, a Public Health Action Plan (PHAP) to Combat Antimicrobial Resistance was released. The PHAP identified actions needed to address the emerging threat of antibiotic resistance and highlighted the need to improve federal agencies' ongoing monitoring of antibiotic use and of antibiotic-resistant infections. Reports on the action plan have subsequently been published annually.

- In 2003, as a result of the "Framework Document" process, FDA published a final guidance document for industry (GFI #152), "Evaluating the Safety of Antimicrobial New Animal Drugs with Regard to their Microbiological Effects on Bacteria of Human Health Concern." The guidance outlines a qualitative risk assessment process for evaluating the safety of antimicrobial drugs intended for use in food-producing animals. The importance of a drug for human medical therapy is a key factor considered in the evaluation.

- In 2004, FDA published a draft risk assessment on the use of streptogramins (Virginiamycin) in animals and the development of Synercid-resistant

GENERAL COMMENTS OF THE DEPARTMENT OF HEALTH AND HUMAN SERVICES (HHS) ON THE GOVERNMENT ACCOUNTABILITY OFFICE'S (GAO) DRAFT REPORT ENTITLED, "ANTIBIOTIC RESISTANCE: AGENCIES HAVE MADE LIMITED PROGRESS ADDRESSING ANTIBIOTIC USE IN ANIMALS" (GAO-11-801)

Enterococcus faecium infections in humans. Comments on the draft risk assessment to assess the link between the use of Virginiamycin in animals and Synercid resistance in humans were received from representatives of the general public, public health professionals, and industry groups.

- In 2004, FDA also conducted a Veterinary Medicine Advisory Committee (VMAC) meeting on the microbial food safety of tulathromycin indicated to treat respiratory disease in cattle and swine. Tulathromycin is related to the macrolide class of drugs which are critically important for treating bacterial infections in humans.

- In 2005, FDA withdrew approval for the use of enrofloxacin in poultry. This animal drug belongs to a class of drugs known as fluoroquinolones which are critically important for treating bacterial infections in humans.

- In 2006, FDA conducted another VMAC meeting on the microbial food safety of injectable cefquinome sulfate for bovine respiratory disease in cattle. Cefquinome is a 4th generation cephalosporin, which is a class of critically important drugs for treating bacterial infections in humans.

- In 2010, FDA published draft guidance for industry (GFI # 209), "The Judicious Use of Medically Important Antimicrobial Drugs in Food-Producing Animals." In that document, FDA provided two guiding principles for the judicious use of antimicrobials in animal agriculture. First, medically important antimicrobial drugs should be limited to uses in food-producing animals that are considered necessary for assuring animal health, which means that they should not be used in healthy animals for production purposes (e.g., to promote growth or improve feed efficiency). Second, the guidance also recommended that medically important antimicrobial drugs be limited to uses in food-producing animals that include veterinary oversight or consultation.

- In 2010, FDA also published the first annual summary report of antimicrobial drug sales and distribution data in compliance with Section 105 of the Animal Drug User Fee Amendments of 2008 (ADUFA). This new provision requires antimicrobial drug sponsors to report to FDA on an annual basis the amount of antimicrobial active ingredient in their drugs that have been sold or distributed for use in food-producing animals. It also requires FDA each year to make summaries of the sales and distribution information received from drug sponsors available to the public.

- In March 2011, a draft revised 2010 PHAP was published for public comment. The draft revised PHAP provides a valuable framework for FDA to work with our federal partners on the issue of antimicrobial resistance.

- 2 -

GENERAL COMMENTS OF THE DEPARTMENT OF HEALTH AND HUMAN SERVICES (HHS) ON THE GOVERNMENT ACCOUNTABILITY OFFICE'S (GAO) DRAFT REPORT ENTITLED, "ANTIBIOTIC RESISTANCE: AGENCIES HAVE MADE LIMITED PROGRESS ADDRESSING ANTIBIOTIC USE IN ANIMALS" (GAO-11-801)

Currently, a number of relevant initiatives are ongoing within FDA including 1) the development of a coordinated strategy for implementing the recommendations outlined in GFI #209, 2) an effort to examine possible mechanisms for enhancing the collection of data that can help track antimicrobial drug use, and 3) the development and implementation of a strategy for enhancing the NARMS program.

One measure of the progress for implementing FDA's strategy for encouraging judicious use of medically important antimicrobial drugs in food-producing animals consistent with GFI #209 is the pace at which medically important antibiotic products are successfully updated to align with the GFI #209 recommendations. Implementation of this strategy is a high priority for FDA. Also, as noted below, FDA is exploring approaches for obtaining additional information related to antimicrobial drug use to enhance the antimicrobial drug sales/distribution data that is currently reported to FDA in compliance with Section 105 of the Animal Drug User Fee Amendments of 2008 (ADUFA). Such additional information will assist in tracking the progress of steps taken to support the judicious use of these important drugs.

Addressing antimicrobial resistance is a challenging task that requires the expertise and collaborative efforts of many entities. FDA continues to utilize a multi-pronged approach for addressing concerns about the use of antimicrobial drugs in animal agriculture. The agency is working diligently to phase in key changes with the cooperation of the animal health industry and is exploring other regulatory tools to help support the goal of assuring the judicious use of medically important antimicrobial drugs in food-producing animals. FDA is collaborating with other relevant government agencies and is seeking input from its stakeholders to develop a sound strategy for addressing this important public health issue.

FDA offers the following additional comments regarding GAO's recommendations:

GAO Recommendation No. 1

To track the effectiveness of policies to curb antibiotic resistance, including FDA's voluntary strategy designed to reduce antibiotic use in food animals and to address action items in the surveillance focus area of the 2001 interagency plan, we recommend the Secretaries of Agriculture and Health and Human Services direct agencies to, consistent with their existing authorities, (1) identify potential approaches for collecting detailed data on antibiotic use in food animals, including the species in which antibiotics are used and the purpose for their use, as well as the costs, time frames and potential tradeoffs associated with each approach; (2) collaborate with industry to select the best approach; (3) seek any resources necessary to implement the approach; and (4) use the data to assess the effectiveness of policies to curb antibiotic resistance.

GENERAL COMMENTS OF THE DEPARTMENT OF HEALTH AND HUMAN SERVICES (HHS) ON THE GOVERNMENT ACCOUNTABILITY OFFICE'S (GAO) DRAFT REPORT ENTITLED, "ANTIBIOTIC RESISTANCE: AGENCIES HAVE MADE LIMITED PROGRESS ADDRESSING ANTIBIOTIC USE IN ANIMALS" (GAO-11-801)

FDA Response

FDA generally agrees with this recommendation and recognizes that having more detailed data to help track trends in antibiotic use in food-producing animals would benefit the overall effort to assure the judicious use of these drugs. This information can be helpful when analyzing trends in antimicrobial resistance observed through the NARMS program and can provide an indication of changes in antibiotic use practices in response to the implementation of judicious use strategies.

Given the limitations of the antimicrobial drug sales and distribution data currently reported to FDA annually in compliance with Section 105 of the Animal Drug User Fee Amendments of 2008 (ADUFA), the agency is exploring potential approaches for obtaining more detailed sales and distribution information or other information on actual drug use. FDA intends to consult with USDA and seek opportunities where the agencies could collaborate on strategies for addressing this issue.

GAO Recommendation No. 2

To enhance surveillance of antibiotic-resistant bacteria in food animals, we recommend that the Secretaries of Agriculture and Health and Human Services direct agencies to, consistent with their existing authorities, modify NARMS sampling to make the data more representative of antibiotic resistance in food animals and retail meat throughout the United States.

FDA Response

In 2007, the FDA Science Board completed a detailed review of the NARMS program and provided a number of recommendations. With these recommendations in mind, FDA developed a draft strategic plan for pursuing a number of key enhancements to the NARMS program, many of which have been implemented or are being developed.

Based on the 2007 FDA Science Board review, FDA published the *NARMS Strategic Plan* for public comment on January 24, 2011. The key strategic goals outlined in this plan include, 1) to develop, implement and optimize a shared database, with advanced data acquisition and reporting tools; 2) to make sampling more representative and more applicable to trend analysis; 3) to strengthen collaborative research projects to address high risk food safety issues; and 4) to support international activities which promote food safety, and mitigate the spread of antimicrobial resistance.

In July 2011, FDA held a public meeting to discuss this strategic plan with particular focus on ways to improve the current sampling approach. Based on this input, FDA intends to work collaboratively with CDC and USDA on moving forward with enhancements to the NARMS program.

GENERAL COMMENTS OF THE DEPARTMENT OF HEALTH AND HUMAN SERVICES (HHS) ON THE GOVERNMENT ACCOUNTABILITY OFFICE'S (GAO) DRAFT REPORT ENTITLED, "ANTIBIOTIC RESISTANCE: AGENCIES HAVE MADE LIMITED PROGRESS ADDRESSING ANTIBIOTIC USE IN ANIMALS" (GAO-11-801)

We note that on page 19 of the draft report, GAO states that, *Due to its nonrandom selection of states, FDA cannot determine the extent to which NARMS retail meat samples are representative of the United States.* It is true that the participating states are not selected randomly, but instead volunteer to participate in the program. Therefore, some regions of the country are not represented in the NARMS retail meat program. We do not believe that samples need to be statistically representative of the entire US to serve as indicators of U.S. retail meat.

GAO Recommendation No. 3

To better focus future federal research efforts on alternatives to current antibiotic use practices, we recommend that the Secretaries of Agriculture and Health and Human Services direct agencies to (1) assess previous research efforts on alternatives and identify gaps where additional research is needed, in collaboration with the animal production industry; and (2) specify steps in the draft 2010 interagency plan that agencies will take to fill those gaps.

FDA Response

FDA agrees that an important component of an overall strategy for curbing the development of antimicrobial resistance is to encourage the use, where possible, of alternatives to antibiotics for treating, controlling, or preventing disease in animals. Although some of these alternatives, such as the use of vaccines in animals or alternative management practices, are beyond the scope of FDA's authority, FDA is committed to working collaboratively with other agencies such as USDA/ARS on this important issue.

GENERAL COMMENTS OF THE DEPARTMENT OF HEALTH AND HUMAN SERVICES (HHS) ON THE GOVERNMENT ACCOUNTABILITY OFFICE'S (GAO) DRAFT REPORT ENTITLED, "ANTIBIOTIC RESISTANCE: AGENCIES HAVE MADE LIMITED PROGRESS ADDRESSING ANTIBIOTIC USE IN ANIMALS" (GAO-11-801)

We note that on page 19 of the draft report, GAO states that, *Due to its nonrandom selection of states, FDA cannot determine the extent to which NARMS retail meat samples are representative of the United States.* It is true that the participating states are not selected randomly, but instead volunteer to participate in the program. Therefore, some regions of the country are not represented in the NARMS retail meat program. We do not believe that samples need to be statistically representative of the entire US to serve as indicators of U.S. retail meat.

GAO Recommendation No. 3

To better focus future federal research efforts on alternatives to current antibiotic use practices, we recommend that the Secretaries of Agriculture and Health and Human Services direct agencies to (1) assess previous research efforts on alternatives and identify gaps where additional research is needed, in collaboration with the animal production industry; and (2) specify steps in the draft 2010 interagency plan that agencies will take to fill those gaps.

FDA Response

FDA agrees that an important component of an overall strategy for curbing the development of antimicrobial resistance is to encourage the use, where possible, of alternatives to antibiotics for treating, controlling, or preventing disease in animals. Although some of these alternatives, such as the use of vaccines in animals or alternative management practices, are beyond the scope of FDA's authority, FDA is committed to working collaboratively with other agencies such as USDA/ARS on this important issue.

GENERAL COMMENTS OF THE DEPARTMENT OF HEALTH AND HUMAN SERVICES (HHS) ON THE GOVERNMENT ACCOUNTABILITY OFFICE'S (GAO) DRAFT REPORT ENTITLED, "ANTIBIOTIC RESISTANCE: AGENCIES HAVE MADE LIMITED PROGRESS ADDRESSING ANTIBIOTIC USE IN ANIMALS" (GAO-11-801)

We note that on page 19 of the draft report, GAO states that, *Due to its nonrandom selection of states, FDA cannot determine the extent to which NARMS retail meat samples are representative of the United States.* It is true that the participating states are not selected randomly, but instead volunteer to participate in the program. Therefore, some regions of the country are not represented in the NARMS retail meat program. We do not believe that samples need to be statistically representative of the entire US to serve as indicators of U.S. retail meat.

GAO Recommendation No. 3

To better focus future federal research efforts on alternatives to current antibiotic use practices, we recommend that the Secretaries of Agriculture and Health and Human Services direct agencies to (1) assess previous research efforts on alternatives and identify gaps where additional research is needed, in collaboration with the animal production industry; and (2) specify steps in the draft 2010 interagency plan that agencies will take to fill those gaps.

FDA Response

FDA agrees that an important component of an overall strategy for curbing the development of antimicrobial resistance is to encourage the use, where possible, of alternatives to antibiotics for treating, controlling, or preventing disease in animals. Although some of these alternatives, such as the use of vaccines in animals or alternative management practices, are beyond the scope of FDA's authority, FDA is committed to working collaboratively with other agencies such as USDA/ARS on this important issue.

- 5 -

End Notes

[1] GAO, Food Safety: The Agricultural Use of Antibiotics and Its Implications for Human Health, GAO/RCED-99-74 (Washington, D.C.: Apr. 28, 1999).

[2] GAO, Antibiotic Resistance: Federal Agencies Need to Better Focus Efforts to Address Risk to Humans from Antibiotic Use in Animals, GAO-04-490 (Washington, D.C.: Apr. 22, 2004).

[3] See, most recently, GAO, High-Risk Series: An Update, GAO-11-278 (Washington, D.C.: February 2011).

[4] See: GAO, Federal Food Safety Oversight: Food Safety Working Group Is a Positive First Step but Governmentwide Planning Is Needed to Address Fragmentation, GAO-11-289 (Washington, D.C.: Mar. 18, 2011).

[5] GAO-04-490.

[6] FDA Science Advisory Board, National Antimicrobial Resistance Monitoring System (NARMS) Program Review (May 25, 2007).

[7] For more information, see GAO, Antibiotic Resistance: Data Gaps Will Remain Despite HHS Taking Steps to Improve Monitoring, GAO-11-406 (Washington, D.C.: June 1, 2011).

[8] GAO-04-490.

[9] GAO, Veterinarian Workforce: Actions are Needed to Ensure Sufficient Capacity for Protecting Public and Animal Health, GAO-09-178 (Washington, D.C.: Feb. 4, 2009).

[10] GAO, Executive Guide: Effectively Implementing the Government Performance and Results Act, GAO/GGD-96-118 (Washington, D.C.: June 1996).

[11] A land-grant university is an institution that has been designated by its state legislature or Congress to receive unique federal support, including funds for cooperative extension offices. Land-grant universities are directed by law to offer public education programs based on the results of university research, including research and education related to agriculture issues.

[12] For more information on USDA's efforts to prepare for outbreaks of highly pathogenic avian influenza, see GAO, Avian Influenza: USDA Has Taken Steps to Prepare for Outbreaks, but Better Planning Could Improve Response, GAO-07-652 (Washington, D.C.: June 11, 2007).

[13] Avoparcin was never approved for food animal use in the United States.

[14] GAO, Food Safety: Selected Countries' Systems Can Offer Insights into Ensuring Import Safety and Responding to Foodborne Illness, GAO-08-794 (Washington, D.C.: June 10, 2008).

[15] Denmark, Sweden, France, the Netherlands and the United Kingdom collected antibiotic use data by species. Germany, Norway, Finland, Switzerland, and the Czech Republic collected more general data on antibiotic use. Norway and Switzerland are not EU countries, but they are nevertheless sharing data about antibiotic use.

[16] Austria, Belgium, Cyprus, Estonia, Hungary, Ireland, Italy, Lithuania, Luxembourg, Poland, Portugal, and Spain.

End Note for Appendix II

[1] USDA officials noted that there is no guarantee that animals raised using alternative modes of production contain no antibiotic-resistant bacteria.

In: Antibiotic Resistance
Editors: R. Finley and M. Solomon
ISBN: 978-161942-416-6

Chapter 2

ANTIBIOTIC USE IN AGRICULTURE: BACKGROUND AND LEGISLATION*

Geoffrey S. Becker

SUMMARY

Public health experts have expressed concern about an increase in antibiotic resistance among sick patients. Such resistance has been linked to a number of causes, such as overuse of antibiotics by medical professionals and their patients, and their wide use for nontherapeutic (essentially nonmedical) purposes in food animals. Agricultural producers administer antibiotics in feed for some types of food-producing animals not only to treat and prevent diseases, but also to encourage growth and efficient use of feed rations. Some argue that nontherapeutic uses should be severely constrained and/or limited to drugs not associated with human medical treatments. Others oppose this approach, arguing that many animal production operations would not be commercially viable (and that the animals' health could be compromised) without the drugs' routine use, and/or that the linkage between such use and antimicrobial resistance lacks a strong scientific basis.

In the 111th Congress, companion bills (H.R. 1549, S. 619) have been introduced that would phase out the nontherapeutic use in food animals of seven specific classes of antibiotic drugs that can also be used to treat or prevent diseases and infections in humans. While not directly

---

* This is an edited, reformatted and augmented version of a Congressional Research Service publication, CRS Report for Congress R40739, from www.crs.gov, dated January 7, 2010.

endorsing the bills, a top official of the U.S. Food and Drug Administration (FDA), which regulates animal drugs under the Federal Food, Drug, and Cosmetic Act, recommended in July 2009 that the phase-out of nontherapeutic uses of animal antibiotics be considered.

Some supporters of the bills have urged that they be incorporated into other pending legislation (for example, H.R. 2749, a food safety bill approved in June 2009 by the House Energy and Commerce Committee). Others, including some members of the House Agriculture Committee, have expressed strong opposition to the antibiotics bills and their inclusion in any food safety legislation.

At Issue

Increased resistance of microbial pathogens to the various antimicrobial drugs developed to treat them is a widely recognized public health problem.[1] Most scientific and public health experts agree that the problem is linked to a number of causes, including over-prescription of antimicrobial drugs by medical practitioners, their misuse by patients, releases into the environment, and—at the root of all of these reasons—the ability of the pathogens themselves to evolve and adapt rapidly.

Another reason for resistance can be the use of antimicrobials or, more specifically, antibiotics, in food-producing animals. However, stakeholders disagree on the extent of agriculture's contribution to the problem and on the strength of scientific evidence of such a linkage.

A number of bills have been introduced in recent years aimed at curtailing agricultural uses of medically significant antibiotics, but none have been enacted. The issue is again being debated in the 111th Congress, where new bills (H.R. 1549, S. 619) are pending. Top officials of the U.S. Food and Drug Administration (FDA) weighed in on the debate in July 2009 by expressing support in concept for phasing out nontherapeutic (essentially, nonmedical) uses of antimicrobials in food animal production. Whether a bill will advance beyond the hearing stages remains to be seen, however; many, including those with large agricultural constituencies, oppose these bills.

Current Legislative Proposals

Companion bills to restrict the use of medically significant antibiotics in food animals were introduced in the House and Senate on March 17, 2009, as

H.R. 1549 by Representative Slaughter and S. 619 by Senator Reid (for Senator Kennedy). These bills, the Preservation of Antibiotics for Medical Treatment Act of 2009 (PAMTA), are similar in title and purpose to bills introduced but not enacted in the 110th Congress (H.R. 962, S. 549), the 109th Congress (H.R. 2562, S. 742), the 108th Congress (H.R. 2932, S. 1460), and the 107th Congress (H.R. 3804, S. 2508).

The currently pending bills (H.R. 1549, S. 619) would amend the key FDA authorizing law—the Federal Food, Drug, and Cosmetic Act (FFDCA, 21 U.S.C. 301 et seq.)—to require the Secretary of Health and Human Services (HHS, under which FDA is located) to withdraw, within two years, the approval of any "nontherapeutic use" in food-producing animals of a "critical antimicrobial animal drug." Such action would be required unless the Secretary determines, in writing, that the holder of an approved application (i.e., the drug's sponsor) has demonstrated, or a risk analysis has found, "that there is a reasonable certainty of no harm to human health due to the development of antimicrobial resistance that is attributable in whole or in part to the nontherapeutic use of the drug." The HHS Secretary also would be required to refuse a new application for a critical antimicrobial animal drug if the sponsor failed to demonstrate the same "reasonable certainty" standard.

The bills would define a "critical antimicrobial animal drug" to be one that "is intended for use in food-producing animals" and is composed wholly or partly of "any kind of penicillin, tetracycline, macrolide, lincosamide, streptogramin, aminoglycoside, or sulfonamide," or "any other drug or derivative of a drug that is used in humans or intended for use in humans to treat or prevent disease or infection caused by microorganisms."

With respect to such drugs, the bills would define the term "nontherapeutic use" as "any use of the drug as a feed or water additive for an animal in the absence of any clinical sign of disease in the animal for growth promotion, feed efficiency, weight gain, routine disease prevention, or other routine purpose."

H.R. 1549 was the subject of a hearing in the House Rules Committee.[2] Neither the House nor the Senate version otherwise advanced during the first session of the 111th Congress. Supporters have considered seeking to attach the bills to pending food safety or health reform legislation, but have not done so at this time.[3]

Another antimicrobial resistance bill, the "Strategies to Address Antimicrobial Resistance Act" (STAAR, H.R. 2400, introduced May 13, 2009, by Representative Matheson), takes a different approach to the issue of antimicrobial resistance. H.R. 2400 would apply broadly to all antimicrobials and to a variety of uses, including in human health care, not just to antimicrobials used in food animals. The bill, which had been introduced in the 110th Congress as H.R. 3697, would establish an Antimicrobial Resistance Office within the HHS Secretary's office as well as a public health advisory board to channel advice and expertise on the issue, and would reauthorize a number of antimicrobial resistance programs authorized in a previous law that have since expired, among other things.[4] The bill has not advanced.

ADMINISTRATION VIEWS

The Obama Administration has not taken a position on the PAMTA or STAAR bills, but HHS officials have suggested that a phase-out of the use of antimicrobials for growth promotion and/or feed efficiency may be considered. "Eliminating these uses will not compromise the safety of food," an FDA official told Congress in July 2009. Noting that the agency's current statutory authority for withdrawing a new animal drug approval "is very burdensome," he stated that any proposed legislation should "facilitate the timely removal of nonjudicious uses of antimicrobial drugs in food-producing animals."[5]

At the same time, he added, FDA believes that some antimicrobial uses for disease prevention "are necessary and judicious to relieve or avoid animal suffering and death." However, he noted a number of factors that should be considered in weighing the need for such a use and stated that "FDA also believes that the use of medications for prevention and control should be under the supervision of a veterinarian."[6] In practical terms, this would mean that animal antimicrobials that are currently available over the counter would no longer be, although whether a prescription would be needed in all situations remains unclear.[7]

USE OF ANTIBIOTICS IN AGRICULTURE[8]

Types of Use

Antibiotics are used in food-producing animals for three major reasons, according to HHS's Centers for Disease Control and Prevention (CDC).[9] First, they are used in high doses for short periods of time to treat sick animals. Second, they are used—also in high doses for short periods of time—to prevent diseases during times when animals may be more susceptible to infections (for example, after weaning, or during transport). This use "usually involves treating a whole herd or flock, which increases the likelihood of selecting for organisms that are resistant to the antibiotic." Finally, "antibiotics are commonly given in the feed at low doses for long periods to promote the growth of cattle, poultry, and swine. In the 1950s studies showed that animals given low doses of antibiotics gained more weight for a given amount of feed than untreated animals. Exactly how this occurs is still greatly unknown."[10]

Animal drugs may be administered either by injecting them directly or by mixing them into feed and water. The latter method may be viewed as more efficient when treating large groups of animals, and it is the only feasible approach for some species such as poultry and fish.[11]

Citing USDA survey data from 1999, McEwen and Fedorka-Cray observed that approximately 83% of feedlots administered at least one antibiotic for disease prevention or growth promotion, including control of liver abscesses, accelerated weight gain, and prevention of respiratory disease outbreaks. Other feedlot uses were for a variety of individual animal or group treatments such as for diarrhea and pneumonia. Cow-calf producers, however, used antimicrobials relatively little. Milk replacers to feed veal calves could contain antimicrobials for disease prevention; lactating dairy cattle could receive antimicrobial injections to treat or prevent mastitis. Poultry were administered antimicrobials to treat, control, or prevent a number of problematic diseases such as necrotic enteritis (an intestinal infection) and *E. coli* infections; several types were also approved and widely used mainly for growth promotion and feed efficiency in broilers, egg layers, and turkeys. For swine, antimicrobial use was mainly in feed at relatively low concentrations for growth promotion or disease prevention, particularly after weaning. Swine received antimicrobials either individually or in feed to treat or prevent pneumonia, bacterial diarrhea caused by such organisms as *E. coli* and *Clostridium perfringens*, swine dysentery, and ileitis.[12]

Long-term, low-dose treatments may serve as a prophylactic against diseases, particularly where animals are housed in large groups in close confinement facilities. Such facilities are very widely used in commercial swine, poultry, and egg production and are increasingly being adopted in the dairy and beef cattle industries. On the one hand, animal confinement facilities provide for closer and more cost-effective management of animals, protection from the elements and predators, and increased biosecurity (protection from outside pathogens, whether unintentionally or intentionally introduced).

On the other hand, the concentrated nature of such agricultural operations means that a disease, if it occurs, can spread rapidly and become quickly devastating—increasing the need to rely on antibiotics as a preventive measure.

Table 1. Examples of Antibiotics Commonly Used in Animals (feedlot cattle, swine, broiler chickens)

Antibiotic Class	Animal Use	Human Medicine Importance
Cephalosporin (3rd gen.)	disease treatment in cattle and swine	critical
Fluoroquinoline	disease treatment in cattle	critical
Penicillins	disease treatment in cattle; growth, disease treatment in swine	high
Macrolide	disease treatment and prevention in cattle; growth, disease treatment and prevention in swine	critical
Phenicol	disease treatment and prevention in cattle	not
Sulfonamide	growth in swine	not
Tetracycline	disease treatment and prevention in cattle; growth, disease treatment and prevention in swine	high
Lincosamide	disease treatment in swine	high
Pleuromutilin	growth in swine	not
Polypeptide	growth in swine; growth promotion, disease prevention in chickens	not
Streptogramin	growth, disease prevention in chickens	high
Carbadox	growth in swine	not
Bambermycin	growth, disease prevention in chickens	not

Source: Adapted from GAO, Antibiotic Resistance: Federal Agencies Need to Better Focus Efforts to Address Risk to Humans from Antibiotic Use in Animals, Appendix V. Rankings of human medicine importance are GAO's, based on FDA determinations.

Notes: With regard to human medicine importance, FDA ranks antibiotics as "critically important" ("critical" in the above table), "highly important" ("high" in the table), or "important." The ranking is based on five criteria from the most important (it is used in treating pathogens that cause foodborne disease) to the least important (there is difficulty in transmitting resistance across genera and species). See the discussion under "Regulatory Approach" later in this report.

Antibiotics work by interfering with some part of the necessary biological mechanisms of bacteria to kill them directly or to halt their growth. They are broadly divided into classes based on their chemical structures and modes of action. Classes include a "lead" antibiotic as initially discovered, and modified versions of it, including improvements designed to overcome developing resistance to it. (See *Table 1.)* After penicillin was first clinically tried in the 1930s (and mass-produced in the 1940s), antibiotic development and usage in both animal and human populations, generally of the same types of drugs, grew steadily. By the 1950s antibiotics came into even wider use as livestock growth promoters.[13]

Amount of Use

Reliable data on total U.S. antibiotic use do not appear to be publicly available. A 2001 report by the Union of Concerned Scientists (UCS), a science-based advocacy organization, stated that 24.6 million pounds of antibiotics were used for nontherapeutic purposes in food animals annually. The organization asserted that this represented 70% of all antibiotics produced in the United States in one year.[14] Others including the Animal Health Institute (AHI), which represents companies that market animal drugs and other animal health products, counter that the UCS figures are based on questionable assumptions and estimates (in part, because no publicly reliable data appear to have been developed). Also, the UCS counts in the total such substances as ionophores, which are used as growth promoters in animals but have never been used in human medicine, AHI has noted.[15]

UCS includes disease prevention in its definition of nontherapeutic use along with growth promotion. Others have taken issue with this definition. The American Veterinary Medical Association (AVMA) has argued: "The term 'non-therapeutic' has no meaning in federal regulation or common usage. The FDA approves antimicrobials for four purposes: disease treatment, disease prevention, disease control, and growth promotion/feed efficiency. The FDA does not approve antimicrobials for 'non-therapeutic' uses."[16] The last AHI survey of its members reported that 87% of the antibiotics used in all animals (including nonfood animals such as pets) were for disease treatment, control, and prevention.[17] A policy statement on antibiotic usage by the American Public Health Association (APHA) asserts that as much as 40% of all antibiotics used in the United States are added into feeds to promote efficient growth, but no source is provided for this figure.[18]

Seeking more useful data, lawmakers included a provision in the Animal Drug User Fee Amendments of 2008 that requires drug sponsors to submit an annual report to the HHS Secretary for each approved antimicrobial drug that is sold or distributed for use in food-producing animals. The annual report must contain such details as the amount of the active ingredient and the quantities distributed domestically and exported. The Secretary is required to make summaries of the information available to the public. The first annual report for currently approved antibiotics must be submitted no later than March 31, 2010.[19]

Citing data inadequacies, Representative Slaughter on September 21, 2009, asked the Government Accountability Office (GAO) to examine these questions:

- What data exist on the types and quantities of antibiotics used in food animals and on the purposes for which they are used?
- What further data do USDA, FDA, and CDC believe are needed to assess and mitigate the risks to humans from antibiotic use in animals and what efforts are underway or are needed to collect these data?
- To what extent is USDA monitoring food animals and meat for the emergence of antibiotic-resistant strains of pathogens, such as *E. coli*, *Campylobacter*, *Salmonella*, and *Listeria*?
- How effectively is FDA overseeing industry compliance with currently approved animal antibiotics and uses for these antibiotics?
- What is FDA's plan and time frame for reevaluating the antibiotics (and antibiotic uses) that it has approved for animals?
- What efforts have USDA, FDA, and CDC taken to assess the human health risks related to antibiotic use in animals, and what have the assessments shown?[20]

PUBLIC HEALTH CONCERNS

Approximately 2 million people acquire bacterial infections each year in U.S. hospitals alone. Approximately 90,000 die as a result, and 63,000, or 70%, of these deaths are from infections resistant to one or more antimicrobial drugs.[21] Antimicrobial resistance is a natural phenomenon associated with use of antimicrobial drugs and began to be recognized soon after penicillin was first used. However, strains that acquire an ability to survive a drug and to multiply have been subject to wider scientific study.[22] According to the CDC:

> Bacteria become resistant to antibiotics through several mechanisms. Through their ability to share genetic information, bacteria can transfer resistant genes to one another. Some bacteria develop the ability to neutralize an antibiotic before it can do them harm, others can rapidly pump the antibiotic out, and still others can change the antibiotic attack site so it cannot affect the function of the bacteria. In addition, bacteria that were at one time susceptible to an antibiotic can acquire resistance through mutation of their genetic material or by acquiring pieces of DNA that code for the resistance properties from other bacteria. The DNA that codes for resistance can be grouped in a single easily transferable package called a plasmid. Bacteria can become resistant to many antimicrobial agents because they can acquire multiple antibiotic resistant plasmids.23

Antimicrobial use in animals has contributed to the emergence of antimicrobial-resistant microorganisms but is by no means the only cause. Many scientists believe that the misuse and overuse of antimicrobials in human medicine have greatly accelerated antimicrobial resistance. Physicians may prescribe the drugs too frequently or for the wrong reasons (e.g., prescribing antibiotics to treat viral infections, which do not respond to the drugs). Patients may not complete their prescribed courses of an antimicrobial, making it more likely the surviving microbes will develop resistance.[24] Sometimes, antimicrobials are used as preventive measures, for example, before surgeries to ward off infections or prior to travel to avert traveler's diarrhea. Hospital medical staff appear to contribute to resistance through improper sanitary practices like inadequate hand washing or instrument cleaning.

Another route of resistance is the release of antibiotics into the environment (e.g., through runoff from farm waste). Studies have found that some pharmaceuticals, including antibiotics, are not completely used in human or other animal bodies and can be passed into the sewage system, where treatment does not break them down completely. Significant concentrations of certain drugs have been reported in drinking water, for example. Testimony presented in 2008 to a Senate committee cited several studies that found antimicrobial-resistant bacteria in groundwater sampled near hog farms.[25]

Many foodborne bacteria that can cause disease in humans, such as *Salmonella*, *Campylobacter*, and strains of *E. coli* including O157:H7, are found in the intestinal tracts of healthy food-producing animals like swine, poultry, and cattle. According to FDA, "When an animal is treated with an antimicrobial drug, a selective pressure is applied to all bacteria exposed to the drug. Bacteria that are sensitive to the antimicrobial are killed or put at a competitive disadvantage, while bacteria that have the ability to resist the antimicrobial have an advantage and are able to grow more rapidly than the more susceptible bacteria."[26] Resistant bacteria can then be transferred to the human population through either direct contact with the animals or through consumption of improperly handled food from them. FDA "believes that human exposure through the ingestion of antimicrobial resistant bacteria from animal-derived foods represents the most significant pathway for human exposure to bacteria that have emerged or been selected as a consequence of antimicrobial drug use in animals."[27]

According to FDA, an estimated 80% of the estimated 2.5 million annual human cases of illness from campylobacteriosis are foodborne, and 95% of the 1.4 million annual human cases from non-typhoidal salmonellosis are foodborne. When the bacteria are also resistant to antimicrobial drugs, public health can be compromised. For example, despite regulatory restrictions on the use of two FDA-approved fluoroquinolone products, ciprofloxacin-resistant *Campylobacter* were found in 20% of retail chicken product samples. Further, molecular subtyping showed an association between resistant strains of bacteria found in chicken products and in human cases of campylobacteriosis.[28]

In 1996 the CDC began a new effort to collect antimicrobial resistance data in collaboration with FDA and the U.S. Department of Agriculture (USDA). The effort, the National Antimicrobial Resistance Monitoring System (NARMS) for Enteric Bacteria, is charged with monitoring antimicrobial resistance among foodborne bacteria isolated from humans. The most recent published report includes surveillance data for 2006 for clinical non-Typhi *Salmonella*, *Salmonella* ser. Typhi, *Shigella*, *Campylobacter*, and *E. coli* O157 isolates.[29] The NARMS reported that:

- 19.6% (160 out of 816) of *Campylobacter* isolates were resistant to the fluoroquinolone ciprofloxacin, compared with 12.9% (28 out of 217) in 1997;
- 2.7% (60 out of 2,184) of non-Typhi *Salmonella* isolates were resistant to the quinolone nalidixic acid, compared with 0.4% (5 out of 1,324) in 1996;

- 3.6% (79 out of 2,184) of non-Typhi *Salmonella* isolates were resistant to the third-generation cephalosporin ceftiofur, compared with 0.2% (2 out of 1,324) in 1996;
- 54.0% (175 out of 324) of *Salmonella* ser. Typhi isolates were resistant to the quinolone nalidixic acid, compared with 19.2% (32 out of 167) in 1999.

FDA has observed that "[d]efinitive answers about the safety of antimicrobial use in animals remain scientifically challenging, but more information is accumulating that raises concerns about food safety." The agency also cited earlier studies from the Netherlands, the United Kingdom, and Spain indicating temporal relationships between ciprafloxin-resistant *Campylobacter* and approval of fluoroquinolones for food-producing animals, for example.[30]

Others believe that the scientific evidence regarding the relationship between animal antibiotics use and human health risk is subject to differing interpretations. The AVMA, while acknowledging the need for prudent use of such drugs, has called such evidence "limited and conflicting."[31] The organization and others argue that leveling a ban on those now in use, particularly before conducting additional studies and risk-based evaluations, would be detrimental to both animal and human health.

The AVMA and others have pointed to the experience in Europe, where the European Union (EU) phased out antimicrobials for animal growth promotion as of January 1, 2006.[32] Among EU members, Denmark implemented a voluntary ban on the use of antimicrobials for growth promotion in 1998 and a mandatory ban in 2000. This ban, which was not extended to the use of these drugs for control and treatment of disease, "has not resulted in significant reduction of antibiotic resistance patterns in humans. It has, however, resulted in an increase in disease and death in swine herds and an increase in the use of antimicrobials for therapeutic uses in swine herds that discontinued the use of antibiotic growth promoters," according to the AVMA.[33]

Such observations are based on data published in annual reports on the antimicrobial situation by the Danish government.[34] Others have offered differing interpretations of the data. The Pew Environment Group reported that an updated assessment of the impacts of Denmark's ban shows that although therapeutic use of antibiotics increased slightly after the ban, it has leveled off since 2003, and total antibiotic consumption has decreased significantly. The assessment also shows limited if any long-term effects on overall productivity in the swine herd, and a decrease in antimicrobial resistance has followed reduced use.[35]

Meanwhile, the United States is participating with other member countries in a Codex Alimentarius Commission Ad Hoc Intergovernmental Task Force on Antimicrobial Resistance aimed at helping to develop guidelines to assess human health risks associated with the presence of antimicrobial resistant agents transmitted through food and feed. Codex, which established the task force in 2006, is the international standards body for food safety. The United States in September 2009 submitted its comments on proposed draft guidelines to be discussed at an October 2009 task force meeting in Korea.[36]

REGULATORY APPROACH

The FDA's Center for Veterinary Medicine (CVM) is responsible for regulating the manufacture and distribution of drugs and food additives for all animals, including food animals, under authority of the Federal Food, Drug, and Cosmetic Act (FFDCA), as amended.[37] CVM approves new animal drugs, using criteria similar to those in the approval process for human medicines, with the intent of ensuring their safety and effectiveness.

Generally, animal drug approval, including for antimicrobials, is conducted under two processes. The first process involves the submission by the drug's manufacturer or sponsor of an application for an investigational new animal drug (INAD) exemption to conduct pre-approval clinical trials. The second process is the new animal drug application (NADA) review. The review includes the evaluation not only of its safety and effectiveness for the intended animal, but also, for a food animal, its safety to humans who might consume food from the animal. Among the required tests for an animal drug not required for a human one is how much time is necessary for drug residues to leave the animal's body (withdrawal time), to ensure that antibiotic residues are not in food products made from it. A new animal drug product cannot be marketed without NADA approval.[38]

The FDA issued in October 2003 a guidance document reflecting its "current thinking" regarding its assessment of the safety to humans of antimicrobial animal drugs.[39] *Evaluating the Safety of Antimicrobial New Animal Drugs with Regard to Their Microbiological Effects on Bacteria of Human Health Concern* (Guidance #152) focuses specifically on food safety, and in particular on the risk that foodborne pathogens that contaminate these products will be resistant to antimicrobial drugs that were used in the food-producing animal. The guidance does not address other effects of antimicrobial animal drug use, such as from environmental runoff, or the question of antimicrobial residues that may be present in the food products. The latter hazard is addressed in several other FDA guidance documents.

An assessment of the potential public health effects of the use of antimicrobial animal drugs is challenging in at least three ways. First, drug sponsors cannot readily explore potential public health effects of animal drugs through premarket clinical trials, as the trials are not conducted on humans. Second, antimicrobial resistance is a hazard that sometimes develops only after an antimicrobial drug is approved and becomes widely used; it is not necessarily a hazard that exists and can be studied during the approval process. Third, the causal pathways by which uses of an antimicrobial animal drug may lead to antimicrobial resistance in microbial pathogens, and thereby cause or worsen human illness, are often poorly understood, or may be difficult to document because relevant data are not available. Guidance #152 is the agency's effort to clarify, for drug sponsors, its approach to these challenges, using qualitative risk assessment.

Guidance #152 provides a step-wise approach that comports with international standards.[40] First, FDA recommends that drug sponsors submit a hazard characterization, providing basic information about the drug, its uses and mechanisms of action, mechanisms for the emergence of resistance in target and non-target microbes, the importance of the drug in human medicine, the state of scientific information and knowledge gaps about the drug and antimicrobial resistance, and related information. Based on the hazard characterization, FDA could potentially (1) provide more specific guidance regarding the conduct of the subsequent risk assessment; (2) determine that a risk assessment was not necessary to demonstrate the drug's safety; or (3) determine that such a demonstration was not likely to be made, and that the application was not likely to succeed.

Next, the three steps in the qualitative risk assessment are (1) a *release assessment* to estimate the probability that the proposed use of the antimicrobial new animal drug in food-producing animals will result in the emergence or selection of resistant bacteria in the animal; (2) an *exposure assessment* of the likelihood of human exposure to foodborne bacteria of human health concern through particular exposure pathways, in this case through foods of animal origin; and (3) a *consequence assessment* regarding the importance of the antimicrobial animal drug or its analogs in human medicine, though a sponsor may use alternate data if it believes it to be more current or otherwise superior. This process yields an FDA ranking of each antimicrobial drug according to its importance in human medicine, as "critically important," "highly important," or "important." Outputs are then to be integrated into an overall risk estimation, using a matrix provided in the guidance. The risk estimation would yield an overall assessment of the public health risk associated with the proposed conditions of use of the drug, ranked as high (Category I), medium (Category II), or low (Category III).

Guidance #152 says that an advisory committee may be convened to evaluate the applications of Category I and selected Category II antimicrobial animal drugs. The guidance then lays out a risk management strategy for approved antimicrobial animal drugs, noting that even a Category I classification would not necessarily result in the denial of approval, but would likely require appropriate (and perhaps more stringent) risk management steps. These steps may include limiting the conditions, including duration, of use; requiring veterinary supervision (versus, for example, over-the-counter marketing); prohibiting extra-label uses;[41] and postmarket monitoring of microbial resistance to the drug, possibly through NARMS.

After Guidance #152 was published, FDA convened its Veterinary Medicine Advisory Committee (VMAC) in September 2006 to consider an application for cefquinome, an antibiotic to be used in beef cattle. The drug's sponsor presented its risk assessment according to the guidance, concluding that the proposed uses placed the drug in Category II (medium risk), and recommending that the drug be approved, with certain postmarket risk management steps. The VMAC instead voted against approving the drug. FDA, which does not have to abide by the committee's recommendation, had not approved the drug as of December 2009.

The trajectory of the cefquinome application highlights the challenging and evolving regulatory approach to the safety of antimicrobial animal drugs. The drug's sponsor reached a conclusion of medium risk using guidance that it called conservative, leaning toward greater safety when evidence was insufficient. Consumer representatives asserted that the guidance should have given the drug a higher consequence risk ranking, which would have yielded a higher overall risk ranking.[42] Industry representatives asserted that members of the committee strayed from the methodical constraints of the guidance in reaching their individual conclusions.

The FDA also has developed a series of species-specific educational materials for veterinarians based on 15 AVMA-developed "Guidelines for the Judicious Therapeutic Use of Antimicrobials." These guidelines range from employing where possible non-drug preventive strategies such as appropriate husbandry and hygiene to using the narrowest-spectrum antimicrobials whenever appropriate.[43] At its annual meeting on July 10, 2009, the AVMA House of Delegates reportedly voted to create a steering committee to reassess its policy regarding judicious use, a process that could take a year to complete.[44]

End Notes

[1] The term "antimicrobial" refers broadly to drugs that act against a variety of microorganisms, including bacteria, viruses, fungi, and parasites. The term "antibiotic," or "antibacterial," refers to a drug that is used to treat infections caused by bacteria. Antibiotics are, therefore, types of antimicrobial drugs. The issues discussed in this report involve principally, but not exclusively, antibiotic drugs. The terms "antibiotic" and "antimicrobial" are often used interchangeably in policy discussions, and in this report.

[2] U.S. Congress, House Committee on Rules, *H.R. 1549—Preservation of Antibiotics for Medical Treatment Act of 2009*, 111th Cong., 1st sess., July 13, 2009.

[3] See, for example, Ben Moscovitch, "Lawmaker, Stakeholders Try Rallying Support for Animal Antibiotic Ban," *FDA Week*, December 4, 2009.

[4] This paragraph is based in part on material in a CRS congressional distribution memo, "Comparison of Selected Bills in the 110th Congress Regarding Animal Drug Use and Antimicrobial Resistance," dated June 9, 2008, by Sarah A. Lister, Specialist in Public Health and Epidemiology.

[5] Joshua M. Sharfstein, FDA Principal Deputy Commissioner of Food and Drugs, July 13, 2009, testimony before the House Committee on Rules; and Linda Tollefson, FDA Assistant Commissioner for Science, June 28, 2008, testimony before the Senate Committee on Health, Education, Labor, and Pensions.

[6] Sharfstein testimony.

[7] See, for example, "New Administration First to Let FDA Take Strict Stance on Antibiotics," *FDA Week*, July 24, 2009. Some antimicrobials approved for use in food animals may be purchased over the counter by producers. Other require greater oversight, including veterinary prescriptions with varying requirements, depending on the drug, its intended use, and stipulations associated with its approval.

[8] Portions of this report are adapted from out-of-print CRS Report RL30814, *Antibiotic Resistance: An Emerging Public Health Issue*, by Donna U. Vogt and Brian A. Jackson. Another source is Government Accountability Office (GAO, then called the General Accounting Office), *Antibiotic Resistance: Federal Agencies Need to Better Focus Efforts to Address Risk to Humans from Antibiotic Use in Animals* (GAO-04-490), April 2004.

[9] Antibiotics also are used in plant agriculture, primarily sprayed in orchards as a prophylactic treatment for diseases. Although use data are somewhat limited, this use appears to be limited. Source: Anne K. Vidaver, "Uses of Antimicrobials in Plant Agriculture," *Clinical Infectious Diseases*, 2002:34, Supplement 3, pp. S107-S110.

[10] CDC, "Antibiotic Resistance 101," posted on its web page, "Get Smart: Know When Antibiotics Work on the Farm," at http://www.cdc.gov/narms/get_smart.htm.

[11] Scott A. McEwen and Paula J. Fedorka-Cray, "Antimicrobial Use and Resistance in Animals," *Clinical Infectious Diseases*, 2002:34, Supplement 3, pp. S93-S106.

[12] McEwen and Fedorka-Cray.

[13] CDC, "Landmarks in Antibiotic Use," posted on its web page, "Get Smart: Know When Antibiotics Work on the Farm," at http://www.cdc.gov/narms/get_smart.htm.

[14] Union of Concerned Scientists, *Hogging It: Estimates of Antimicrobial Abuse in Livestock*, January 2001.

[15] AHI, e-mail communication, July 20, 2009.

[16] Christine Hoang, DVM, MPH, AVMA, September 25, 2008, testimony before the House Agriculture Subcommittee on Livestock, Dairy, and Poultry.

[17] AHI, e-mail communication, July 20, 2009.

[18] APHA, "Antibiotic Resistance Fact Sheet," accessed July 21, 2009, at http://www.apha.org/advocacy/reports /facts/advocacyfactantibiotic.htm.

[19] Section 105 of P.L. 110-316, signed into law August 14, 2008. Other proposals in the 110th Congress would have provided for more extensive data requirements. See CRS Report RL34459, *Animal Drug User Fee Programs*, by Sarah A. Lister.

[20] The letter was posted on the Representative's website and accessed September 30, 2009, at http://www.louise.house.gov/index.php?option=com_content&view=article&id=1306:slaughter-asks-gao-foradditional-data-on-antibiotic-use-in-animals&catid=41:press-releases&Itemid=109. See also the discussion in the next section on the work of the existing National Antimicrobial Resistance Monitoring System for Enteric Bacteria.

[21] Sharfstein testimony; Tollefson testimony.

[22] See, for example, J. F. Acar and G. Moulin, "Antimicrobial resistance at farm level," *Rev. sci. tech. Off. int. Epiz.*, 2006, 25(2), 775-792.

[23] CDC, "Antibiotic Resistance 101."

[24] Sharfstein testimony.

[25] Jay P. Graham, Research Fellow at the Johns Hopkins Bloomberg School of Public Health, June 28, 2008 testimony before the Senate Health, Education, Labor, and Pensions Committee.

[26] FDA, Center for Veterinary Medicine (CVM), *Judicious Use of Antimicrobials for Swine Veterinarians*, and *Judicious Use of Antimicrobials for Poultry Veterinarians*, http://www.fda.gov/AnimalVeterinary/ SafetyHealth/AntimicrobialResistance/default.htm.

[27] FDA, *Evaluating the Safety of Antimicrobial New Animal Drugs with Regard to Their Microbiological Effects on Bacteria of Human Health Concern*, Guidance for Industry #152, October 23, 2003, p. 3.

[28] *Judicious Use of Antimicrobials for Swine Veterinarians*, and *Judicious Use of Antimicrobials for Poultry Veterinarians*. In 2005, FDA withdrew its approval of Baytril, a fluoroquinolone related to the human drug Cipro, in poultry (which it first proposed to do in 2000), after it concluded that the drug played a role in promoting antibiotic resistance among *Campylobacter* infections in humans. See http://www.fda.gov/ AnimalVeterinary/ SafetyHealth/RecallsWithdrawals/ucm042004.htm.

[29] Data can be accessed at http://www.cdc.gov/NARMS/.

[30] *Judicious Use of Antimicrobials for Swine Veterinarians*, and *Judicious Use of Antimicrobials for Poultry Veterinarians*.

[31] AVMA, "Judicious Therapeutic Use of Antimicrobials," accessed July 21, 2009, at http://www.avma.org/issues/ jtua/default.asp.

[32] This phase-out is delineated under Article 11 of European Parliament and Council Regulation No. 1831/2003, on additives for use in animal nutrition, at http://eur-lex.europa.eu/LexUriServ/LexUriServ.do?uri =OJ:L:2003: 268:0029:0043:EN:PDF.

[33] Lyle Vogel, DVM, MPH, DACVM, AVMA, June 24, 2008, testimony before the Senate Health, Education, Labor, and Pensions Committee.

[34] The most recent report is DANMAP 2007—Use of antimicrobial agents and occurrence of antimicrobial resistance in bacteria from food animals, foods and humans in Denmark. DANMAP is the Danish acronym for the Danish Integrated Antimicrobial Resistance Monitoring and Research Programme. The annual reports can be accessed at http://www.danmap.org/.

[35] Robert P. Martin, Senior Officer of the Pew Environment Group and former Executive Director of the Pew Commission on Industrial Farm Animal Production, July 13, 2009 testimony before the House Rules Committee. Martin's testimony states that these new findings recently had been presented to a producers conference in Kansas by a Danish health official and would be published later in 2009 in the Journal of the AVMA.

[36] For information and links, see the FSIS September 9, 2009, news release "Public Meeting to Address Agenda Items for the 3rd Session of the Codex Ad Hoc Intergovernmental Task Force on Antimicrobial Resistance," at http://www.fsis.usda.gov/News_&_ Events/NR_ 090909_01/index.asp.

[37] Primary authority is at FFDCA § 512 [21 U.S.C. 360(b)].

[38] FFDCA § 512(d), regarding review of animal drug applications, provides grounds for denying approval, including tests that show the drug is unsafe, or the determination that there is insufficient information as to whether the drug is safe. Applicable regulations are at 21 CFR 514.1(b)(8). For a fuller explanation of the approval process, see Appendix B of CRS Report RL34459, *Animal Drug User Fee Programs*, by Sarah A. Lister.

[39] The following discussion of Guidance #152 is adapted from material prepared in 2008 by Sarah A. Lister, CRS Specialist in Public Health and Epidemiology. The guidance document can be viewed at this FDA web page: http://www.fda.gov/downloads/ AnimalVeterinary/GuidanceComplianceEnforcement/GuidanceforIndustry/UCM052519. pdf.

[40] FDA cites a 2001 method for antimicrobial risk analysis published by the Office of International Epizootics (OIE), the international animal health standard-setting and harmonization organization, of which the United States is a member.

[41] "Extra-label use," which is similar to "off-label use" of drugs in humans, is defined by FDA (at 21 C.F.R. 530) as "[a]ctual use or intended use of a drug in an animal in a manner that is not in accordance with the approved labeling. This includes, but is not limited to, use in species not listed in the labeling, use for indications (disease and other conditions) not listed in the labeling, use at dosage levels, frequencies, or routes of administration other than those stated in the labeling, and deviation from labeled withdrawal time based on these different uses." Such use is by definition a prescription drug use, and is only permitted within the scope of a valid veterinarian-client-patient relationship. Extra-label use is limited to circumstances when the health of an animal is threatened by failure to treat; therefore, extra-label use to enhance production is prohibited.

[42] Martin of the Pew Environment Group stated in his House testimony that most animal antibiotics in nontherapeutic use were approved before the FDA began considering the resistance question, and that the agency has not established a schedule for reviewing existing approvals, even though Guidance #152 notes the importance of doing so.

[43] For details see http://www.fda.gov/AnimalVeterinary/SafetyHealth/Antimicrobial Resistance/ JudiciousUseof Antimicrobials/default.htm.

[44] "AVMA votes to reassess antimicrobial policy," *Food Chemical News*, July 27, 2009.

In: Antibiotic Resistance
Editors: R. Finley and M. Solomon
ISBN: 978-161942-416-6

Chapter 3

ANTIBIOTIC RESISTANCE: DATA GAPS WILLREMAIN DESPITE HHS TAKING STEPS TO IMPROVE MONITORING*

United States Government Accountability Office

WHY GAO DID THIS STUDY

Infections that were once treatable have become more difficult to treat because of antibiotic resistance. Resistance occurs naturally but is accelerated by inappropriate antibiotic use in people, among other things. Questions have been raised about whether agencies such as the Department of Health and Human Services (HHS) have adequately assessed the effects of antibiotic use and disposal on resistance in humans. GAO was asked to (1) describe federal efforts to quantify the amount of antibiotics produced, (2) evaluate HHS's monitoring of antibiotic use and efforts to promote appropriate use, (3) examine HHS's monitoring of antibiotic-resistant infections, and (4) describe federal efforts to monitor antibiotic disposal and antibiotics in the environment, and describe research on antibiotics in the development

* This is an edited, reformatted and augmented version of The United States Government Accountability Office publication, Report to the Committee on Agriculture, House of Representatives GAO-11-406, dated June 2011.

of resistance in the environment. GAO reviewed documents and interviewed officials, conducted a literature review, and analyzed antibiotic sales data.

What GAO Recommends

To better control the spread of resistance, GAO recommends that HHS's Centers for Disease Control and Prevention (CDC) develop and implement strategies to improve its monitoring of (1) antibiotic use and (2) antibiotic-resistant infections. HHS generally agreed with our recommendations. HHS, the Environmental Protection Agency (EPA) and the Department of the Interior (DOI) provided technical comments, which we incorporated as appropriate.

What GAO Found

Federal agencies do not routinely quantify the amount of antibiotics that are produced in the United States for human use. However, sales data can be used as an estimate of production, and these show that over 7 million pounds of antibiotics were sold for human use in 2009. Most of the antibiotics that were sold have common characteristics, such as belonging to the same five antibiotic classes. The class of penicillins was the largest group of antibiotics sold for human use in 2009, representing about 45 percent of antibiotics sold.

HHS performs limited monitoring of antibiotic use in humans and has implemented efforts to promote their appropriate use, but gaps in data on use will remain despite efforts to improve monitoring. Although CDC monitors use in outpatient healthcare settings, there are gaps in data on inpatient antibiotic use and geographic patterns of use. CDC is taking steps to improve its monitoring, but gaps such as information about overall antibiotic use will remain. Because use contributes to resistance, more complete information could help policymakers determine what portion of antibiotic resistance is attributed to human antibiotic use, and set priorities for action to control the spread of resistance. CDC's Get Smart program promotes appropriate antibiotic use; CDC has observed declines in inappropriate prescribing, but it is unclear to what extent the declines were due to the program or to other factors. CDC's program has been complemented by efforts by the National

Institutes of Health and the Food and Drug Administration, such as supporting studies to develop tests to quickly diagnose bacterial infections.

Gaps in CDC's monitoring of antibiotic-resistant infections limit the agency's ability to assess the overall problem of antibiotic resistance. There are data gaps in monitoring of such infections that occur in healthcare facilities; CDC does not collect data on all types of resistant infections to make facilitywide estimates and the agency's information is not nationally representative. CDC can provide accurate national estimates for certain resistant infections that develop in the community, including tuberculosis. Although CDC is taking steps to improve its monitoring, these efforts will not allow CDC to accurately assess the overall problem of antibiotic resistance because they do not fill gaps in information. Without more comprehensive data, CDC's ability to assess the overall scope of the public health problem and plan and implement preventive activities will be impeded.

Federal agencies do not monitor the disposal of most antibiotics intended for human use, but they have detected them, as well as antibiotics for animal use, in the environment, which results partly from their disposal. EPA and DOI's United States Geological Survey have examined the presence of certain antibiotics in environmental settings such as streams. Studies conducted by scientists have found that antibiotics present in the environment at certain concentrations can increase the population of resistant bacteria.

ABBREVIATIONS

ABCs	Active Bacterial Core Surveillance
ANDA	Abbreviated New Drug Application
CCL	Contaminant Candidate List
CDC	Centers for Disease Control and Prevention
CMS	Centers for Medicare & Medicaid Services
DOI	Department of the Interior
EIP	Emerging Infections Programs
EPA	Environmental Protection Agency
FDA	Food and Drug Administration
GISP	Gonococcal Isolate Surveillance Project
HAI	healthcare-associated infection
HHS	Department of Health and Human Services
MDRO	multidrug-resistant organism
MIC	minimum inhibitory concentration

MRSA	Methicillin-resistant *Staphylococcus aureus*
NAMCS	National Ambulatory Medical Care Survey
NARMS:	EB National Antimicrobial Resistance Monitoring System: Enteric Bacteria
NCQA	National Committee for Quality Assurance
NDA	New Drug Application
NHAMCS	National Hospital Ambulatory Medical Care Survey
NHSN	National Healthcare Safety Network
NIH	National Institutes of Health
NNDSS	National Notifiable Diseases Surveillance System
NTSS	National Tuberculosis Surveillance System
PhRMA	Pharmaceutical Research and Manufacturers of America
RCRA	Resource Conservation and Recovery Act
SDWA	Safe Drinking Water Act
TB	tuberculosis
UCMR	Unregulated Contaminant Monitoring Rule
USGS	United States Geological Survey
USITC	United States International Trade Commission

June 1, 2011

The Honorable Frank D. Lucas
Chairman

The Honorable Collin Peterson
Ranking Member
Committee on Agriculture
House of Representatives

Over 60 years ago penicillin was the first antibiotic introduced to treat bacterial infections, leading to a dramatic drop in deaths from bacterial infections that were previously untreatable, as well as significant gains in life expectancy. The eventual emergence and spread of bacterial infections that are resistant to antibiotics, however, has jeopardized these gains because infections that were once easy to cure with antibiotics are becoming difficult, if not impossible, to treat. Some bacterial infections, such as certain types of pneumonia and gonorrhea that are acquired in the community, have developed resistance to almost all currently available antibiotics. Furthermore, the bacterial infections that contribute most to human disease are also those in which antibiotic resistance is most common, such as respiratory tract infections and infections acquired in hospitals. Although not all infections acquired in hospitals are resistant to antibiotics, individuals with resistant infections are more likely to have a poor prognosis and to remain in the hospital for a longer time, resulting in greater medical costs.[1]

While the development of antibiotic resistance is not new, as resistance is a natural biological phenomenon and can occur when any antibiotic is present, it is accelerated by a variety of factors including the inappropriate use of antibiotics in the absence of a bacterial infection and the prolonged use of antibiotics to treat patients who are critically ill. Antibiotic-resistant bacteria that are present in the human body can be spread to others. In addition, antibiotic-resistant bacteria that occur in the environment, either from natural causes or their discharge into soil or bodies of water, may spread their resistance to other bacteria.

Scientists, public health officials, and clinicians agree that antibiotic resistance has become a national and global health challenge. While there are various causes of antibiotic resistance—including the use of antibiotics in humans and animals—the actual scope of the overall problem is not clear and there is uncertainty about the relative contributions of each cause.[2] Recommendations for government action to address antibiotic resistance have been made by various organizations and scientific experts, including a task force made up of federal agencies, and there is agreement that, among other things, improved surveillance of antibiotic use and antibiotic-resistant infections is needed to adequately understand antibiotic resistance and implement effective strategies to help control this complex problem.[3] Further, a congressional committee[4] and others have made recommendations to increase the geographic coverage of existing federal agency surveillance to address concerns such as gaps in the ability to track and monitor certain antibiotic-resistant infections, such as methicillin-resistant *Staphylococcus aureus* (MRSA).

Questions have been raised as to whether federal agencies, including the Department of Health and Human Services (HHS), have adequately assessed the relationship among the volume of antibiotics produced for human use, the human use of antibiotics, the presence of antibiotics in the environment, and the problem of antibiotic resistance. The House Committee on Agriculture asked us to evaluate how federal agencies track the occurrence of antibiotic resistance and the use and disposal of antibiotics into the environment. In this report, we (1) describe efforts by federal agencies to quantify the amount of antibiotics produced for human use, (2) describe and evaluate HHS efforts to monitor antibiotic use and promote the appropriate use of antibiotics by humans, (3) examine HHS efforts to monitor cases of antibiotic-resistant infections in humans in the United States, and (4) describe federal efforts to monitor the disposal of antibiotics intended for human use, federal efforts to monitor the presence of antibiotics in the environment, and the scientific evidence regarding the role of antibiotics in the development of antibiotic-resistant bacteria in the environment.

To describe efforts to quantify the amount of antibiotics produced for human use by federal agencies, we interviewed HHS officials to determine whether HHS collects information about, and quantifies, the amount of antibiotics that are produced for human use. We also reviewed documents from HHS and the U.S. International Trade Commission (USITC)—a federal agency that collects and analyzes trade data to inform U.S. trade policy—to learn about federal efforts to quantify antibiotic production in the United States. We purchased 2009 national sales data for antibiotics from IMS Health to estimate the volume of antibiotics produced in the United States for human use.[5] IMS Health provided us the total volume of antibiotics, in kilograms, that were sold, based on all antibiotic drugs that were included in the Red Book Advanced database, as of April 2010.[6] We converted the total volume from kilograms to pounds. To further describe the antibiotics that were sold in 2009, we classified the total volume of antibiotics by antibiotic class, the route of administration (e.g., oral), and the types of pharmacies that purchased antibiotics (e.g., chain store pharmacy). To assess the reliability of IMS Health data, we reviewed existing information about the data and interviewed officials knowledgeable about the data to assess their completeness.[7] We determined that the data were sufficiently reliable for their use in this report.

To describe HHS efforts to monitor the use of antibiotics in humans, we reviewed HHS documents and interviewed HHS officials. We reviewed HHS documents describing the various surveys that HHS uses to routinely collect data about antibiotic use, including information about the survey samples, the types of data that are gathered, and how antibiotic use is measured. We also reviewed agency documents that summarize trends in antibiotic use, based on the surveys. We interviewed HHS officials with responsibility for the surveys about the strengths and limitations of each survey and how the agency uses the collected data to monitor antibiotic use. To evaluate HHS's efforts to monitor antibiotic use, we compared HHS's data collection and monitoring activities with broad guidelines for monitoring antibiotic use, which we identified by reviewing relevant HHS documents and expert organization (e.g., World Health Organization) guidelines. To describe HHS efforts to promote the appropriate use of antibiotics, we reviewed documents from HHS about programs and activities focused specifically on decreasing inappropriate antibiotic use. We also interviewed officials from HHS about the objectives and implementation of these programs and activities. To evaluate HHS's efforts to promote the appropriate use of antibiotics, we reviewed relevant HHS documents and research articles in peer-reviewed journals about the effectiveness of intervention programs to reduce inappropriate antibiotic use and we interviewed HHS officials about the strengths and limitations of its program to promote appropriate antibiotic use and how the agency has evaluated its program.

To examine HHS efforts to monitor cases of antibiotic-resistant infections in humans, we reviewed agency documents from HHS and interviewed HHS officials and representatives from an HHS advisory committee on healthcare infection control. We reviewed HHS documents describing each of the agency's surveillance systems that are used to monitor antibiotic resistance. The documents described the purpose and objectives of each system, and what surveillance data are collected and how the data are collected; the documents also provided annual summary information about monitored infections. We interviewed HHS officials with responsibility for each of the surveillance systems about the strengths and limitations of each system and how the data gathered by each system are used by the agency. We also interviewed four members of a federal advisory committee that provides guidance to HHS regarding infection control, surveillance, and prevention, as well as officials from three organizations that serve as liaisons to the committee, to obtain their opinions of the strengths and limitations of HHS's surveillance systems.[8]

To describe federal efforts to monitor the disposal of antibiotics intended for human use, we interviewed officials from the Environmental Protection Agency (EPA), HHS, and the Department of the Interior's (DOI) United States Geological Survey (USGS) to determine if these agencies collect data about the disposal of antibiotics and, if applicable, how they use such data for monitoring. We also reviewed relevant federal laws under which EPA may have responsibility to regulate disposal of certain antibiotics and to monitor certain antibiotics in drinking water, as well as a Food and Drug Administration (FDA) consumer guidance document describing recommended disposal practices for unused drugs. We interviewed officials from the Pharmaceutical Research and Manufacturers of America (PhRMA) to learn about the drug disposal practices that are commonly used by pharmaceutical manufacturers.[9] To describe federal efforts to monitor the presence of antibiotics found in the environment, we reviewed documents describing relevant studies conducted by EPA and USGS, including methods for selecting study sample sites and the study findings. We focused on the extent to which antibiotics were present in environmental settings, including soil, sediment, and bodies of water, and in certain pathways to the environment, such as waste water in treatment plants. We interviewed EPA and USGS officials to obtain background information and context about the studies as well as EPA's use of the study findings. We also interviewed EPA and USGS officials about their plans for further related studies.

To describe the scientific evidence regarding the role of antibiotics in the development of antibiotic-resistant bacteria in the environment, we conducted a literature review and interviewed agency officials. Our literature review included 105 articles that met defined search criteria on antibiotic resistance in the environment, published on or between January 1, 2007, and July 8, 2010. The articles included those published in peer-reviewed journals. In our review, we analyzed the scientific findings reported about antibiotic concentrations that induce environmental bacteria to become resistant and the ability of environmental bacteria to spread resistance through the transfer of resistance genes. We also interviewed EPA and USGS agency officials to obtain context for the scientific evidence presented in the articles. For a detailed description of our literature review, see appendix I.

We conducted our performance audit from March 2010 to June 2011 in accordance with generally accepted government auditing standards. Those standards require that we plan and perform the audit to obtain sufficient, appropriate evidence to provide a reasonable basis for our findings and conclusions based on our audit objectives. We believe that the evidence obtained provides a reasonable basis for our findings and conclusions based on our audit objectives.

BACKGROUND

Antibiotics and the Development and Spread of Antibiotic-resistant Bacteria

Antibiotics are drugs that are used to treat bacterial infections.[10] Antibiotics work by killing or slowing the growth of bacteria and they are not effective against nonbacterial infections, such as those caused by viruses. Antibiotic resistance is the result of bacteria changing in ways that reduce or eliminate the effectiveness of antibiotics to cure infection. Antibiotic use forces bacteria to either adapt or die in a process known as "selective pressure." Selective pressure means that when an antibiotic is used, some bacteria will be killed by the antibiotic while other bacteria will survive. Bacteria are able to survive, in part, because they have certain genetic material that allows them to avoid the effects of the antibiotic. The surviving bacteria will multiply and pass on to future generations their genetic material that is coded for resistance to antibiotics. Any use of antibiotics—appropriate and inappropriate—creates selective pressure among bacteria. (For more information on resistant bacteria, see app. II).

The inappropriate use of antibiotics, or the additional use of antibiotics that could have been avoided, can occur when healthcare providers prescribe antibiotics when they are not beneficial, such as to treat a viral infection, or when antibiotic treatments are not targeted to the specific bacteria causing the infection.[11] Inappropriate antibiotic use also occurs when healthcare providers do not prescribe the correct antibiotic dose and duration of treatment. Further, inappropriate use includes when patients do not complete a full course of prescribed antibiotics.

Antibiotic Disposal and Pathways for Antibiotics to Enter the Environment

Individual consumers, health care facilities, pharmacies, and pharmaceutical manufacturers dispose of unused antibiotics using various methods. For the purposes of this report, the disposal of antibiotics refers to the discard of unused antibiotics by consumers, companies, and others. Common disposal methods for individual consumers include throwing unused antibiotics in the trash, flushing them down the toilet, and pouring them down the drain.[12] According to EPA officials, healthcare facilities and pharmacies often return unused or expired drugs to contracted companies, known as reverse distributors, for manufacturer credit. The reverse distributor is then instructed by the manufacturer to return the unused drug to the manufacturer, or in most cases, the reverse distributor is instructed to dispose of the drugs. The unused drugs are then most likely incinerated as solid waste, subject to state and local environmental regulations. The federal guidelines on how consumers should properly dispose of their unused drugs, including antibiotics, recommend that consumers dispose of their unused drugs either by returning them through a drug take-back program, where available, or by mixing them with coffee grounds or kitty litter and throwing them in the household trash.[13]

Unused antibiotics intended for human use may enter the environment through various pathways such as sewage systems and landfills, depending upon the method of disposal and other factors. Unused antibiotics enter sewage systems after they are flushed down the toilet or poured down the drain. Unused antibiotics that enter the sewage system then flow to wastewater treatment plants where, if not removed during the treatment process, they are released into the environment, such as in rivers and streams, as wastewater effluent.[14] In addition, some areas may use onsite septic systems to treat wastewater and in these systems wastewater is discharged below the ground's surface.[15] Unused antibiotics that are disposed of in the trash could enter the environment if landfills were to leak. Although modern landfills are designed with liners and systems to limit this process by rerouting leachate, that is, liquid generated in landfills, to wastewater treatment plants, the antibiotics that are contained in the leachate may ultimately enter the environment. This can occur if antibiotics are not removed during the wastewater treatment process. In general, wastewater treatment plants are not designed to remove low concentrations of drug contaminants, such as antibiotics.[16,17]

In addition, antibiotics that have been used by humans to treat infections can also enter the environment. Most used antibiotics enter the sewage systems after they are ingested and excreted by individuals because antibiotics are not fully absorbed by the human body.[18] Like unused antibiotics that enter the sewage systems, used antibiotics flow from sewage systems to wastewater treatment plants and may be released into the environment as wastewater effluent or biosolids. Agricultural manure is another potential source of antibiotics entering the environment; some antibiotics used for agriculture are similar to those used by humans.[19]

Federal Agency Responsibilities

Within HHS, the Centers for Disease Control and Prevention (CDC), FDA, and the National Institutes of Health (NIH) have responsibilities for protecting Americans from health risk, including risk associated with antibiotic-resistant infections. These agencies have a variety of responsibilities related to the surveillance, prevention, and research of infectious disease. CDC has a primary responsibility to protect the public health through the prevention of disease and health promotion. One of CDC's primary roles is to monitor health, and part of this role involves monitoring antibiotic-resistant infections and the use of antibiotics. CDC's statutory authority to conduct such surveillance derives from the Public Health Service Act.[20] Tracking the emergence of antibiotic resistance, and limiting its spread, is also part of CDC's mission. Consistent with this mission, CDC implements prevention strategies, such as educational programs, that are designed to limit the development and spread of antibiotic resistance and the agency monitors antibiotic prescriptions in humans to help reduce the spread of antibiotic resistance.

Part of FDA's responsibility for protecting the public health involves assuring the safety and efficacy of human drugs. FDA reviews and approves labels for antibiotics and provides educational information to consumers and healthcare providers about the appropriate use of antibiotics, and the risk of the development of antibiotic resistance associated with their inappropriate use. FDA also licenses vaccines for use in humans to prevent bacterial infections—including certain antibiotic-resistant infections—as well as viral infections and has the authority for the review of diagnostics, including tests to detect bacterial infections. As the nation's medical research agency, NIH is responsible for conducting and funding medical research to improve human health and save lives. According to its research agenda on antibiotic resistance, NIH supports and conducts research on many aspects of antibiotic resistance, including studies of how bacteria develop resistance, the development of diagnostic tests for bacterial infections that are or are likely to become resistant to antibiotics, as well as clinical trials such as those to study the effective duration for antibiotic treatments.

CDC, FDA, and NIH are also co-chairs of the Interagency Task Force on Antimicrobial Resistance (Task Force)[21] and released A Public Health Action Plan to Combat Antimicrobial Resistance (Action Plan) in 2001.[22] The Action Plan identified actions needed to address the emerging threat of antibiotic resistance and highlighted the need to improve federal agencies' ongoing monitoring of antibiotic use and of antibiotic-resistant infections. Specifically, the Action Plan stated that establishing a national surveillance plan for antibiotic-resistant infections should be a high priority, and that improved monitoring of such infections was needed to identify emerging trends and assess changing patterns of antibiotic resistance as well as to target and evaluate prevention and control efforts. The Action Plan also specifically stated that surveillance of antibiotic use in humans should be a high priority and was needed to better understand the relationship between antibiotic use and antibiotic resistance. For example, identifying a specific pattern of antibiotic use associated with increased antibiotic resistance could support a response from policymakers, such as to affect change in antibiotic use practices. Further, improved antibiotic use monitoring would help identify prevention activities and anticipate gaps in the availability of existing antibiotics effective in treating bacterial infections. A revised draft Action Plan was published for public comment on March 16, 2011.[23]

EPA's mission includes protecting Americans from significant environmental health risks. As part of its role, EPA sets national standards for the disposal of solid and hazardous waste and the quality of drinking water. EPA generally regulates the disposal of waste, including some unused or expired drugs, under the Resource Conservation and Recovery Act (RCRA).[24] EPA also promulgates national requirements for drinking water quality of public water systems under the Safe Drinking Water Act (SDWA). EPA conducts research on topics related to human health and the environment, including research aimed at understanding drug disposal practices and the potential human and ecological health risks of drugs, such as antibiotics, found in the environment.

Within DOI, USGS is responsible for providing scientific information to better understand the health of the environment, including our water resources. USGS conducts large-scale studies to gather information that can provide a basis for evaluating the effectiveness of specific policies; these studies can also be used to support decision making at the local and national levels—for example, decisions related to protecting water quality. In 1998, USGS initiated the Emerging Contaminants Project to improve the scientific understanding of the release of emerging contaminants to the environment, including where these contaminants originate and whether they have adverse effects on the environment. As part of the project, USGS has conducted national studies to measure the presence of unregulated contaminants, including antibiotics, in the environment, and conducts targeted local studies to assess the impact of specific pathways by which antibiotics can enter the environment.

CDC's Monitoring of Antibiotic Resistance in Healthcare and Community Settings

CDC has six surveillance systems that provide information to monitor antibiotic resistance that occurs in healthcare and community settings. According to CDC, public health surveillance is the ongoing and systematic collection, analysis, and interpretation of data for use in the planning, implementation, and evaluation of public health practice.[25] The surveillance systems collect information about antibiotic resistance among certain bacteria that cause infections in humans, and the infections are transmitted either in healthcare settings or in the community. For example, CDC's National Healthcare Safety Network (NHSN) monitors infections that occur in healthcare settings, including those that are resistant to antibiotics, such as MRSA, while CDC's Active Bacterial Core Surveillance (ABCs) system monitors bacterial infections such as meningitis and pneumonia that are spread in the community or in healthcare settings.[26] Table 1 provides information about the purpose of each CDC surveillance system that monitors antibiotic resistance and summarizes the settings in which the monitored infections are spread. (See app. III for additional information about each of the six systems.)

Table 1. CDC's Six Surveillance Systems that Provide Information to Monitor Antibiotic Resistance, by System Purpose and Infection Transmission Setting

Surveillance system	Purpose of surveillance system and role in monitoring antibiotic resistance	Infection transmission setting
National Healthcare Safety Network (NHSN)	To provide a database for healthcare facilities to report their healthcare-associated infection (HAI) and antibiotic resistance surveillance data to allow them to estimate the occurrence of such events, monitor trends, and identify patient safety problems.[a] CDC compiles data on antibiotic resistance across participating facilities.	Spread in healthcare settings, such as from healthcare personnel to patient or from patient to patient.
Active Bacterial Core Surveillance (ABCs) [of the Emerging Infections Programs (EIP) Network][b]	To monitor trends in disease and deaths caused by invasive bacterial infections of public health importance, such as meningitis caused by Neisseria meningitidis. ABCs is also used to monitor trends in antibiotic resistance, track new resistance mechanisms, and evaluate the effect of public health interventions.	Spread in the community, from person to person (e.g., by exchange of respiratory secretions), or in healthcare settings, such as from healthcare personnel to patient or from patient to patient.

Table 1. (Continued)

Surveillance system	Purpose of surveillance system and role in monitoring antibiotic resistance	Infection transmission setting
National Antimicrobial Resistance Monitoring System: Enteric Bacteria (NARMS: EB)	To monitor trends in antibiotic resistance among enteric bacteria from humans and to conduct research to better understand the emergence, persistence, and spread of antibiotic resistance.[c] NARMS: EB is also used to provide data to assist FDA in making decisions related to the approval of safe and effective antibiotic drugs for animals and to promote interventions to reduce resistance.	Spread in the community and in other settings, such as through eating food contaminated with fecal matter or eating undercooked poultry.
Gonococcal Isolate Surveillance Project (GISP)	To monitor trends in antibiotic resistance in Neisseria gonorrhoeae—the bacterium that causes gonorrhea—in order to establish a basis for selecting treatment guidelines for gonorrhea.	Spread in the community, from person to person, through sexual contact.
National Tuberculosis Surveillance System (NTSS)	To monitor national trends in tuberculosis (TB), including groups at risk for TB, and to evaluate outcomes of TB cases. CDC also uses NTSS to monitor antibiotic resistance in Mycobacterium tuberculosis—the bacterium that causes tuberculosis.	Spread in the community, from person to person, by breathing infected air during close contact.
National Notifiable Diseases Surveillance System (NNDSS)	To monitor certain infectious diseases, such as human immunodeficiency virus infection and measles. CDC also uses NNDSS to monitor antibiotic resistance in the bacteria Streptococcus pneumoniae, with a focus on assessing the impact of immunization against invasive Streptococcus pneumoniae infection. Streptococcus pneumoniae causes infections such as pneumonia and meningitis.	Spread in the community, from person to person, such as by exchange of respiratory secretions.

Source: GAO analysis of CDC information and scientific literature.

[a] NHSN also allows facilities to report on 'laboratory-identified' event surveillance data for certain HAIs that are resistant to multiple drugs—such as multidrug-resistant Klebsiella infections—as well as Clostridium difficile infections; such data are more easily obtained because they come primarily from laboratory test results without clinical evaluation of patients. Clostridium difficile infections may develop due to the prolonged use of antibiotics during healthcare treatment.

[b] As part of EIP's Healthcare Associated Infections Surveillance, CDC has monitored Clostridium difficile infections in healthcare and community settings since 2009.

[c] FDA coordinates the NARMS program and works with CDC to manage NARMS: EB, the human component of the program. FDA and the United States Department of Agriculture test for antibiotic-resistant enteric bacteria in retail meats and food animals, respectively. Enteric bacteria are found in the intestinal tracts of humans and animals.

FEDERAL AGENCIES DO NOT ROUTINELY QUANTIFY AMOUNT OF ANTIBIOTICS PRODUCED FOR HUMAN USE, BUT SALES DATA SHOW OVER 7 MILLION POUNDS OF ANTIBIOTICS WERE SOLD IN 2009

Federal agencies do not routinely quantify the amount of antibiotics that are produced in the United States for human use, but sales data, which can be used to estimate the quantity of antibiotic production, show that over 7 million pounds of antibiotics were sold in 2009 for human use in the United States. These data indicate that most of the antibiotics sold have common characteristics, such as belonging to five antibiotic classes.

Federal Agencies Do Not Routinely Quantify the Amount of Antibiotics Produced for Human Use

Federal agencies, including FDA and USITC, do not routinely quantify antibiotic production for human use.27 FDA does collect annual information on the quantity of drugs that manufacturers distribute from new drug application (NDA) and abbreviated new drug application (ANDA) holders, but the data are not readily accessible.28 For each approved drug, NDA and ANDA holders are required to report annually to FDA the total number of dosage units of each strength or potency of the drug that was distributed (e.g., 100,000 5 milligram tablets) for domestic and foreign use.29 This information must be submitted to FDA each year— within 60 days of the anniversary date of approval of the drug application—for as long as the NDA or ANDA is active. The data that NDA and ANDA holders submit to FDA on the quantity of distributed drugs are not readily accessible because, according to an FDA official, they are submitted as part of an annual report in the form of a table and the agency does not enter the data electronically.

In addition, because the anniversary dates of approval vary by NDA and ANDA, the reporting periods are not comparable. For drugs with an active ingredient for which there are multiple NDA and ANDA applications, FDA officials stated that one would also need to aggregate the data across multiple applications in order to determine the total quantity of the particular active ingredient. An FDA official told us that the agency rarely uses these data for analyses of drug utilization, drug safety, and drug shortages because other sources of data provide FDA information that is more detailed and timely about the quantities of certain drugs that are available in the market. For example, FDA uses drug sales data, which are available on a monthly basis, to evaluate and address drug safety and drug shortage problems.30 USITC no longer collects and quantifies antibiotic production, but did so until 1994.31.

Over 7 Million Pounds of Antibiotics Were Sold in 2009 for Human Use and Most Antibiotics Sold Share Common Characteristics

Most of the 7.4 Million Pounds of Antibiotics Sold Fell into Five Antibiotic Classes

In 2009, approximately 7.4 million pounds of antibiotics were sold for human use—which can be used as an estimate of the quantity of antibiotics produced for human use in the United States—and most sold share common characteristics, such as antibiotic classes. Most of the 7.4 million pounds, or about 89 percent, of antibiotics that were sold in 2009 fell into five antibiotic classes: penicillins, cephems, folate pathway inhibitors, quinolones, and macrolides (see table 2). The class of penicillins was the largest group of antibiotics sold in 2009.[32] About 3.3 million pounds of penicillins were sold, which represents 45.2 percent of all antibiotics sold in 2009. Penicillins, such as amoxicillin, are used to treat bacterial infections that include pneumonia and urinary tract infections.

Table 2. Amount of Antibiotics Sold in 2009 and Additional Information, by Antibiotic Class

Antibiotic class	Amount sold (in pounds)	Amount sold (in kilograms)	Percentage of total antibiotics sold	Examples of drugs within antibiotic class	Examples of bacterial infections treated by some drugs within antibiotic class
Penicillins	3,336,890	1,516,768	45.2	Penicillin, Amoxicillin, Oxacillin, Piperacillin	Group A Streptococcal infections, some pneumonia infections caused by Streptococcus pneumoniae, bacterial ear infections, some urinary tract infections caused by Escherichia coli, and some Staphylococcus aureus infections.
Cephems	1,094,681	497,582	14.8	Cephalexin, Cefuroxime, Cefotetan, Cefixime, Ceftriaxone	Skin infections, respiratory tract infections, intra-abdominal infections, gonorrhea, and bacterial meningitis.
Folate Pathway Inhibitors	1,064,456	483,843	14.4	Sulfonamides, Trimethoprim-Sulfa-methoxazole	Urinary tract infections and other types of infections
Quinolones	664,894	302,225	9.0	Ciprofloxacin, Levofloxacin	Urinary tract infections, respiratory tract infections, and other infections.
Macrolides	382,139	173,700	5.2	Erythromycin, Azithromycin	Some respiratory tract infections.

Table 2. (Continued)

Antibiotic class	Amount sold (in pounds)	Amount sold (in kilograms)	Percentage of total antibiotics sold	Examples of drugs within antibiotic class	Examples of bacterial infections treated by some drugs within antibiotic class
Other	844,467	383,849	11.4	Tetracyclines, Oxazolidinones, Amino-glycosides, and other classes	Skin infections and other infections.
Total	7,387,527	3,357,967	100.0		

Source: GAO analysis of IMS Health data and summary of CDC and NIH information.

Notes: Classes are identified according to the Clinical and Laboratory Standards Institute classification system. According to this classification system, certain antibiotic classes can be further classified into subclasses. For example, the cephem class includes the subclass of cephalosporins. The total amount of antibiotics sold does not take into account the dose, which varies by individual antibiotic, or the total number of individuals who were prescribed or treated with antibiotics.

The Majority of Antibiotics Sold for Human Use in 2009 Were for Oral Administration and for Use in Outpatient Settings

Most of the antibiotics that were sold for human use in 2009 were for oral administration and for use in outpatient settings. As shown in table 3, about 6.5 million pounds, or 87.4 percent, of all antibiotics sold for human use in 2009 were intended for oral administration, for example, in the form of pills.[33] Oral forms of antibiotics and injectable forms, such as intravenous injections, together accounted for 99 percent of the total pounds sold.

Table 3. Amount of Antibiotics Sold in 2009, by Route of Administration

Route of administration	Amount sold (in pounds)	Amount sold (in kilograms)	Percentage of total antibiotics sold
Oral	6,454,670	2,933,941	87.4
Injection	854,281	388,310	11.6
Other[a]	78,576	35,717	1.1
Total	7,387,527	3,357,967	100.0

Note: Individual entries may not sum to totals because of rounding.

[a] Examples of other routes include administration by ear drops or inhalation.

Table 4. Amount of Antibiotics Sold in 2009, by Type of Purchaser

Type of purchaser	Amount sold (in pounds)	Amount sold (in kilograms)	Percentage of total antibiotics sold
Chain store pharmacies[a]	3,906,132	1,775,515	52.9
Independent pharmacies[b]	923,770	419,896	12.5
Nonfederal hospitals	852,247	387,385	11.5
Food store pharmacies[c]	745,526	338,876	10.1
Clinics	232,672	105,760	3.1
Long-term care facilities	228,662	103,937	3.1
Federal facilities[d]	219,533	99,788	3.0
Other[e]	278,984	126,811	3.8
Total	7,387,527	3,357,967	100.0

Source: GAO analysis of IMS Health data.

[a] Chain store pharmacies include businesses that consist of four or more stores with the same name that are owned and operated by the same organization.

[b] Independent pharmacies are privately owned pharmacies that operate fewer than four stores.

[c] Food store pharmacies include pharmacies that are located in grocery stores.

[d] Federal facilities include, for example, Department of Veterans Affairs hospitals and public health outpatient facilities.

[e] Other includes mail order pharmacies and pharmacies located in such entities as health maintenance organizations and prisons.

About 5.8 million pounds, or 78.6 percent, of all antibiotics sold for human use in 2009 were purchased by chain store pharmacies, independent pharmacies, food store pharmacies, and clinics (see table 4). This suggests that most of the antibiotics that were purchased in 2009 were intended for use in outpatient settings.

Data Gaps Remain Despite CDC's Efforts to Expand Its Limited Monitoring of Antibiotic Use; CDC, NIH, and FDA Have Implemented Efforts to Promote Appropriate Use

Although CDC annually collects certain national data on antibiotic prescriptions to monitor the use of antibiotics, these data have limitations and do not allow for important analyses. CDC is taking steps to improve its monitoring of antibiotic use by collecting and purchasing additional data, but gaps in information will remain. CDC's Get Smart program promotes the appropriate use of antibiotics and the agency has observed recent national declines in inappropriate antibiotic prescribing; however, it is unclear to what extent its program contributed to the recent declines. NIH and FDA activities have complemented CDC's efforts to promote the appropriate use of antibiotics.

CDC Annually Collects Certain National Data on Antibiotic Prescriptions to Monitor Antibiotic Use, but Data Do Not Allow for Important Analyses

CDC conducts two national health care surveys that gather data, annually, on antibiotic prescribing in outpatient settings—the National Ambulatory Medical Care Survey (NAMCS) and the National Hospital Ambulatory Medical Care Survey (NHAMCS).[34] NAMCS is based on a sample of visits to office-based physicians and community health centers.[35] NHAMCS is based on a sample of visits to emergency and outpatient departments and hospital-based ambulatory surgery locations.[36,37] Both surveys obtain data from healthcare provider records on patient symptoms, provider diagnoses, and the names of specific drugs, including antibiotics, that were prescribed during the patient visits.[38] CDC officials stated that, among their purposes, CDC uses NAMCS and NHAMCS to monitor antibiotic use in outpatient settings for patient conditions that do not usually require antibiotics for treatment, such as antibiotic prescribing rates for upper respiratory infections, such as the common cold.

NAMCS and NHAMCS are limited because they do not capture information about the use of antibiotics in inpatient settings. In inpatient settings, such as hospitals, antibiotics are often used, multiple antibiotics may be used in the same patient, and use may be prolonged. Monitoring overall antibiotic use (i.e., in inpatient and outpatient settings) over time is important for understanding patterns in antibiotic resistance. Information about overall antibiotic use in humans is also needed to routinely assess the contribution that human antibiotic use makes to the overall problem of antibiotic resistance in humans, relative to other contributing factors. For example, monitoring what portion of antibiotic use is attributed to humans versus animals is important to understanding antibiotic resistance. CDC officials told us that more complete information about antibiotic use by humans and animals is needed to help interpret trends from surveillance data and to inform on possible strategies to control the spread of antibiotic resistance, such as through changing antibiotic use practices.

NAMCS and NHAMCS data are further limited because they do not allow the agency to assess geographic patterns in antibiotic prescribing practices in outpatient settings. CDC officials told us that the survey samples were designed to obtain national, not state-level estimates. As a result, CDC cannot currently assess the potential effects of geographic variation at the state level in antibiotic prescribing rates on patterns of antibiotic resistance or identify states or other geographic areas in the United States, for instance, which have higher than average antibiotic prescribing for conditions that do not usually require antibiotics for treatment. Information about geographic variation in antibiotic prescribing would allow CDC to anticipate future patterns in antibiotic resistance, given that the use of antibiotics has a direct effect on antibiotic resistance. Such information, according to CDC officials, would also allow CDC to target prevention efforts, such as those aimed at reducing inappropriate antibiotic use.

CDC Is Taking Steps to Improve Its Monitoring of Antibiotic Use in Outpatient and Inpatient Settings, but Gaps in Information Will Remain

CDC is taking steps to improve its monitoring of antibiotic use, but gaps in information about the use of antibiotics will remain. To address the agency's lack of data on inpatient antibiotic use, CDC is planning to gather information on antibiotic use with a prevalence survey of U.S. acute care hospitals in 2011.[39] The survey will be conducted during a single time period on a single day and will collect some patient information about the reasons for the antibiotic use, which include treating an active infection or using antibiotics to prevent infection associated with a medical or surgical procedure.[40] According to CDC officials, these data will fill in the gap in its data by providing information about the prevalence of inpatient antibiotic use. CDC officials further stated that having data on the baseline amount of inpatient antibiotic use, and the reasons for that use, will allow the agency to target and evaluate its own prevention efforts.[41] However, the survey findings will not be representative of hospitals nationwide, because the survey sample is limited to selected hospitals located within five entire states and urban areas in five other states.[42] Furthermore, CDC officials do not know if the survey will be repeated.[43] Without periodic data collection and monitoring, CDC cannot assess trends in inpatient antibiotic use or evaluate the effects that changes in antibiotic use may have on antibiotic resistance.

Additionally, in 2011, CDC officials told us that the agency plans to reinstate a module of NHSN that will allow participating facilities to report their inpatient antibiotic use, which will provide CDC with some inpatient antibiotic use data, but these data will not be nationally representative.[44] In 2009, CDC temporarily discontinued this module because, according to CDC officials, it was not sustainable due to the high burden on facilities to report such data.[45] CDC has redesigned the module to reduce the reporting burden on facilities; for example, CDC officials told us that, instead of relying on manual entry, facilities will be able to electronically capture and automatically send their data to NHSN.[46] While the module will allow facilities in NHSN to monitor their own antibiotic use, the data will not provide the agency with information about the prevalence of inpatient antibiotic use because NHSN is not based on a nationally representative sample of facilities.

To improve CDC's monitoring of antibiotic use in outpatient settings, CDC officials told us that they are finalizing a contract with a private data vendor to obtain 5 years of national data on antibiotic prescribing in outpatient settings by antibiotic drug, county, and type of provider. According to CDC officials, these data will help the agency understand relationships between antibiotic use and antibiotic resistance in certain geographic areas. CDC officials further stated that these data would help guide the agency's prevention efforts. With preliminary data on outpatient prescriptions for the antibiotic subclass of fluoroquinolones, CDC has shown wide variation in prescribing across states. Further, CDC plans to increase the size of the NAMCS sample at least fourfold in 2012, which would allow CDC to produce antibiotic prescribing rates for some states that year.[47]

CDC's Get Smart Program Promotes Appropriate Antibiotic Use to Providers and Patients

CDC's Get Smart: Know When Antibiotics Work (Get Smart) program promotes appropriate antibiotic use, which is aimed specifically at healthcare providers, patients, and parents of young children.[48] CDC launched its Get Smart program in 1995 with the overall goal of reducing the increasing rate of antibiotic resistance.[49] The program is primarily focused on upper respiratory infections because, according to CDC, such infections account for over half of all antibiotics prescribed by office-based physicians. The Get Smart program works with partners, such as certain health insurance companies, to develop and distribute educational materials.[50] With the goal of educating healthcare providers and the public, the Get Smart educational materials are aimed directly at these populations. For example, the Get Smart program supported the development of an online training program for healthcare providers to improve their knowledge and diagnosing of middle ear disease. The Get Smart program developed and launched a national media campaign in 2003, in partnership with FDA, to provide a coordinated message on appropriate antibiotic use to the public and this message has been disseminated through print, television, radio, and other media.[51] For example, CDC developed a podcast for parents of young children, available on CDC's Web site, to communicate its message. In the podcast, a pharmacist counsels a frustrated mother about appropriate antibiotic use and symptomatic relief options for her son's cold. Some materials are aimed at healthcare providers with the goal of educating their patients; for example, the Get Smart program developed a prescription pad for symptoms of viral infections. Healthcare providers can use the communication tool to acknowledge patient discomfort and recommend strategies to their patients for the relief of symptoms associated with viral illnesses—without prescribing an antibiotic unnecessarily. The prescription sheet includes the Get Smart logo and provides information for patients about the appropriate use of antibiotics to treat bacterial infections.

CDC has continued to update and expand its materials for the Get Smart program. For example, CDC officials stated that the agency has expanded its educational materials by partnering with Wake Forest University to develop a curriculum for medical students related to appropriate antibiotic prescribing, and the impact of antibiotic use and its inappropriate use on antibiotic resistance, and the agency has developed a continuing education course for pharmacists. CDC officials told us that pharmacists serve as one of the most important health care professionals in promoting appropriate antibiotic use, for example by educating patients about the importance of taking antibiotics exactly as directed. In November 2010, CDC launched another Get Smart program, called Get Smart for Healthcare. This program focuses on improving antibiotic use in inpatient healthcare settings—including hospitals and nursing homes—through antimicrobial stewardship.

CDC Has Observed Declines in Inappropriate Antibiotic Prescribing, but It Is Unclear to What Extent Its Program to Promote Appropriate Antibiotic Use Contributed to Recent Trends

CDC has observed declines in inappropriate antibiotic prescribing in outpatient settings since its Get Smart program began in 1995, but it is unclear to what extent this program contributed to these trends. For example, using NAMCS and NHAMCS data, CDC found about a 26 percent decline in the number of courses of antibiotics prescribed per 100 children younger than 5 years old for ear infections between 1996-1997 and 2006. Further, CDC reported about a 53 percent decrease in the antibiotic prescription rate for the common cold among all persons between 1996- 1997 and 2006.[52] A similar trend in antibiotic prescribing among children has also been observed with data from the National Committee for Quality Assurance (NCQA). NCQA monitors trends in antibiotic prescribing for the purpose of comparing the performance of healthcare plans.[53] NCQA monitors the percentage of children 3 months to 18 years of age who were diagnosed with an upper respiratory infection and did not receive an antibiotic prescription within 3 days of the office visit, and this measure has shown improvement (i.e., percentage increases in appropriate treatment) between 2003 and 2008.[54]

The measures that CDC uses to evaluate the effectiveness of the Get Smart program do not necessarily reflect the effect of the program because they do not capture information about individuals who were exposed to the Get Smart program, compared to those who were not. As a result, it is unclear if the declines in the inappropriate antibiotic prescribing were due to exposure to Get Smart messages and educational materials or from other factors, such as efforts to measure healthcare performance with antibiotic prescribing indicators (e.g., NCQA measures) or the recommended use of influenza vaccines among young children, since 2004.[55] CDC officials told us that they believe the NCQA measures have helped to improve appropriate antibiotic prescribing by improving knowledge of treatment guidelines by physicians and practitioners. In addition, reducing the number of cases of influenza among children is likely to have contributed to declines in inappropriate antibiotic prescriptions because antibiotics are often prescribed in patients with influenza symptoms. The measures that CDC uses to evaluate the effectiveness of the Get Smart program also do not allow CDC to determine, for example, whether declines in inappropriate antibiotic prescribing are attributable to a decrease in demand for antibiotics by patients, or to improved adherence to appropriate prescribing guidelines by healthcare providers. The measures are further limited because they do not allow CDC to determine whether the observed declines are consistent across the United States or are due to decreases in certain geographic areas.

CDC officials told us that they rely on other indicators to demonstrate the effectiveness of the Get Smart Program, such as interest in CDC's Get Smart Web site and media materials. According to these officials, studies examining the impact of educational materials, including Get Smart materials, further demonstrate the effectiveness of the Get Smart program. For example, CDC officials cited a study in Massachusetts where educational materials, including Get Smart materials, were distributed to physicians and their patients in several communities.[56] Findings indicate that in communities where educational and promotional materials about appropriate antibiotic use—including Get Smart materials—were distributed, antibiotic prescribing rates for children declined. Declines were also observed in communities where these educational and promotional materials were not distributed.57 These findings indicate that factors other than educational and promotional materials focused on the appropriate use of antibiotics may also have led to declines in inappropriate antibiotic prescribing. Without information about which are the most effective ways to reduce inappropriate antibiotic prescribing in outpatient and inpatient settings, CDC cannot target its resources on these preventive approaches.

NIH and FDA Activities Have Complemented CDC's Efforts to Promote Appropriate Antibiotic Use

NIH and FDA have complemented CDC's efforts to promote the appropriate use of antibiotics in humans through various activities. NIH supports research specifically aimed at decreasing the inappropriate use of antibiotics as part of its research agenda to target antibiotic resistance. NIH-funded studies focus on establishing appropriate antibiotic treatment courses, using off-patent antibiotics to treat infections, and developing rapid diagnostic tests to help healthcare providers choose an appropriate antibiotic for treatment.58 For example, in 2009, NIH began funding a clinical trial to determine whether the standard 2-week antibiotic treatment course for children with urinary tract infections can remain effective if shortened, thereby decreasing the likelihood of antibiotic resistance and preserving the effectiveness of existing antibiotics.59 In 2007, NIH awarded two 5-year contracts to study whether off-patent antibiotics such as clindamycin and a combination of the drugs trimethoprim and sulfamethoxazole can be used to treat certain skin infections instead of the more recently developed antibiotics, such as Linezolid and Vancomycin, in order to preserve the newer drugs' effectiveness.60 Further, since 2002, NIH has supported the development of a new test to rapidly diagnose TB. It currently takes up to 3 months to accurately diagnose TB and to determine its resistance to antibiotics, according to NIH officials. Findings from a recent clinical trial study reported that, within 2 hours, the new test can diagnose a TB infection and determine if it is resistant to the antibiotic rifampin, which is commonly used to treat TB.61 NIH officials stated that the test is being recommended by the World Health Organization for the early diagnosis of TB and NIH is currently supporting research to improve the test and expand its capabilities.[62]

Research on the development of vaccines for bacterial and viral infections is also part of NIH's research agenda to decrease the inappropriate use of antibiotics, according to an NIH official. An NIH official stated that the agency has funded the discovery and development of several staphylococcal vaccine candidates, for example, through investigator-initiated grants.[63] In addition, an NIH official told us that NIH conducted preclinical animal studies that provided data for the development of a multivalent staphylococcal vaccine candidate, which allowed the candidate to advance to clinical testing.[64] NIH also supports the development of vaccines for viral infections. According to an NIH official, decreasing the occurrence of influenza infections with influenza vaccines may decrease the inappropriate use of antibiotics. Many healthcare providers inappropriately treat viral respiratory infections with antibiotics, so preventing influenza reduces the opportunities for unnecessary antibiotic treatment.[65]

FDA activities also complement CDC's efforts to promote the appropriate use of antibiotics in humans. According to an FDA official, the agency collaborated with CDC on certain Get Smart activities, such as developing an appropriate antibiotic use message for the national media campaign, and amended its drug labeling regulations in 2003 to require that all oral or intravenous antibiotics for human use include additional information on their appropriate use.[66,67] FDA's labeling requirement is intended to encourage physicians to prescribe antibiotics only when clinically necessary and to encourage them to counsel their patients about the proper use of such drugs and the importance of taking them exactly as directed. For example, the amended regulation requires that antibiotic labeling include the statement that "prescribing [the antibiotic] in the absence of a proven or strongly suspected bacterial infection is unlikely to benefit the patient and increases the risk of the development of drug-resistant bacteria."

CDC's Monitoring of Antibiotic-Resistant Infections Has Limitations in Assessing the Overall Problem of Antibiotic Resistance

CDC's monitoring of antibiotic-resistant infections has limitations in assessing the overall problem of antibiotic resistance. The agency's monitoring of antibiotic-resistant infections in healthcare facilities has data gaps that limit CDC's ability to produce accurate national estimates of such infections. For some of these infections monitored by CDC in community settings, in comparison, CDC can provide accurate national estimates. CDC is taking steps to improve its monitoring of antibiotic-resistant infections in healthcare settings, but these efforts will not improve CDC's ability to assess the overall problem of antibiotic resistance.

Data Gaps in CDC's Monitoring of Antibiotic-Resistant Infections in Healthcare Settings Limit Its Ability to Produce Accurate National Estimates

A sample of healthcare facilities that is not representative—and incomplete information about the entire scope of healthcare-associated infections (HAIs) that are resistant to antibiotics—present data gaps that limit CDC's ability to produce accurate national estimates of antibiotic resistant HAIs in healthcare settings. Some infections are acquired as a result of medical treatment in a healthcare setting, such as a hospital or outpatient unit, while others are transmitted in the community, such as respiratory infections that are spread in schools and the workplace. According to CDC officials, healthcare settings contribute to the development of antibiotic resistance because of their high volume of susceptible patients, large number of disease-causing bacteria, and high antibiotic usage. CDC uses NHSN to monitor HAIs,[68] including antibiotic-resistant HAIs, at a national level, but the facilities that participate are not a nationally representative sample. Facility enrollment and participation in NHSN[69] is either voluntary, required because of a state mandate, or obligated as a condition of participation in HHS' Centers for Medicare & Medicaid Services (CMS) Hospital Inpatient Quality

Reporting program.[70] According to CDC officials, as of January 2011, 23 states and territories required, or had plans to require, healthcare facilities to use NHSN for their reporting mandate.[71] As of January 1, 2011, all acute care hospitals participating in the CMS Hospital Inpatient Quality Reporting Program are obligated to report into NHSN central-line associated bloodstream infections for certain procedures[72] from their intensive care units.[73] Although the number of participating facilities has increased substantially, because healthcare facilities enroll voluntarily or by mandate, this group of facilities is not representative of facilities nationwide, as a random sample would be. Participating healthcare facilities in states with mandated participation are more likely to be overrepresented in the sample, while facilities in states without mandates are more likely to be underrepresented.

The data that participating healthcare facilities supply to NHSN do not reflect the full scope of HAIs that occur within these facilities, further limiting CDC's ability to provide accurate national estimates about antibiotic-resistant HAIs.[74] Participating facilities may submit data about different types of HAIs, and this includes information about whether the HAIs are resistant to antibiotics.[75] For example, some facilities report data to NHSN on central-line associated bloodstream infections but not other infection types, such as catheter-associated urinary tract infections.[76] Further, participating healthcare facilities may report HAI data to NHSN for certain units within facilities. For example, participating facilities may report data to NHSN on infections that occur in intensive care units but not those that occur in specialty care areas. CDC depends on the microbiology data provided by participating facilities to determine, among reported cases, the number and percentage of certain types of HAIs with resistance to certain antibiotics.[77] Without an accurate national estimate of antibiotic-resistant HAIs, CDC cannot assess the magnitude and types of such infections that occur in all patient populations (i.e., facilitywide) within healthcare settings.

CDC's Monitoring of Antibiotic-Resistant Infections in Community Settings Can Provide Accurate National Estimates for Some Infections

CDC's monitoring of antibiotic-resistant infections in community settings can provide accurate national estimates of antibiotic-resistant infections that are caused by 5 of the 12 bacteria that the agency monitors. These 5 are captured by two surveillance systems, the National Antimicrobial Resistance Monitoring System for Enteric Bacteria (NARMS: EB) and the National Tuberculosis Surveillance System (NTSS), which collect nationally representative data about certain antibiotic-resistant infections; these infections can occur in community settings.

Both systems employ sampling strategies that can provide accurate national estimates by collecting representative case information from all 50 states.[78] For NARMS: EB, health departments in all 50 states submit a representative sample of four of the five bacteria it monitors—nontyphoidal *Salmonella*, typhoidal *Salmonella*, *Shigella*, and *Escherichia coli* O157 cases to NARMS: EB for antibiotic susceptibility testing. To ensure adequate sample size and a random sample for testing, the health departments systematically select and submit to NARMS: EB every 20th non-typhoidal *Salmonella*, *Shigella*, and *Escherichia coli* O157 case as well as every typhoidal *Salmonella* case received at their laboratories. NARMS: EB cannot produce an accurate national estimate for one of the five bacteria it monitors—*Campylobacter*—because according to CDC officials, the system collects a sample of the bacteria in 10 states.[79] CDC uses NTSS to collect information about each newly reported case of tuberculosis infection in the United States, including information on drug susceptibility results for the majority of cases that test positive for tuberculosis.

CDC's monitoring of other bacteria that cause antibiotic-resistant infections in community settings cannot provide estimates that are nationally representative because they are derived from samples that do not accurately represent the entire United States. Through ABCs, CDC conducts antibiotic resistance surveillance of five[80] infection-causing bacteria—group A and B *Streptococcus*, *Neisseria meningitidis*, *Streptococcus pneumoniae*, and MRSA.[81,82] According to CDC officials, these bacteria cause bloodstream infections, sepsis, meningitis, and pneumonia. ABCs is a collaboration between CDC, state health departments, and universities in 10 states.[83] CDC officials told us that for each identified case of infection within their surveillance populations, the ABCs sites conduct a chart review to collect a variety of information, such as underlying disease and risk factors, vaccination history, and demographic information. This information is entered into a case report form and submitted to CDC along with bacterial isolates for additional testing, including tests for antibiotic resistance.[84]

ABCs' monitoring of cases of resistant infections is limited to surveillance areas in 10 states, and the surveillance areas vary somewhat depending on the infection-causing bacterium that is monitored. For example, *Neisseria meningitidis* is monitored in 6 entire states and in primarily urban areas in 4 other states while MRSA is monitored in 1 entire state and primarily urban areas in 8 other states.[85] According to CDC's Web site, the population included in the ABCs surveillance areas is roughly representative of the U.S. population on the basis of certain demographic characteristics (e.g., race and age) and urban residence. However, ABCs cannot provide estimates that are nationally representative for rural residence, and some experts have raised concerns because of the underrepresentation of rural areas.[86,87] Further, since surveillance is critical to providing early warning of emerging resistance problems, limited geographic coverage among monitored infection-causing bacteria impedes CDC's ability to detect emerging problems.

The Gonococcal Isolate Surveillance Project (GISP), which CDC uses to monitor antibiotic resistance in *Neisseria gonorrhoeae*, the bacterium that causes gonorrhea, cannot provide accurate national estimates of cases of antibiotic-resistant gonorrhea because it collects information only on selected patient populations. Each month, GISP collects case samples from the first 25 men diagnosed with urethral gonorrhea in each participating sexually transmitted disease clinic. The clinics are located in 24 states and they send these samples to designated laboratories for antibiotic susceptibility testing.[88] However, according to CDC officials, most cases of gonorrhea in the United States are not treated in sexually transmitted disease clinics, and are more likely treated in a variety of healthcare settings, such as primary care physicians' offices. Further, since GISP collects information on cases of gonorrhea from male patients only, the data cannot represent the total U.S. population in order to provide an accurate national estimate of resistant gonorrhea cases.[89]

CDC Is Taking Steps to Improve Its Monitoring of Antibiotic-Resistant Infections in Healthcare Facilities, but These Steps Will Not Improve CDC's Ability to Assess the Overall Problem of Antibiotic Resistance

CDC is taking steps to improve its monitoring of antibiotic-resistant infections in healthcare facilities, but CDC's ability to assess the overall problem of antibiotic resistance will not be improved. With a prevalence survey, CDC is planning to collect additional data in 2011 about HAIs, which may provide more comprehensive information about certain types of HAIs that are resistant to antibiotics. According to CDC officials, the survey of U.S.

acute care hospitals—which will also provide data on antibiotic use, as described previously—will allow the agency to more accurately assess the burden of HAIs and antibiotic resistance among those HAIs in healthcare settings.[90] Unlike NHSN, the survey is designed to allow CDC to assess the magnitude and types of HAIs occurring in all patient populations within the sample of acute care hospitals. The survey will collect information about types of infection (e.g., urinary tract infection, bloodstream infection), bacteria causing HAIs, and test results regarding antibiotic resistance. The survey will not collect resistance information for all bacteria that cause HAIs. However, according to CDC officials, the survey will collect resistance information for some of the most common bacteria that cause HAIs, including *Acinetobacter*, *Enterococcus faecalis*, *Enterococcus faecium*, *Escherichia coli*, *Klebsiella*, *Pseudomonas aeruginosa*, and *Staphylococcus aureus*.[91] While the survey may provide more comprehensive information about certain types of HAIs that are resistant to antibiotics because it is designed to cover all patient populations in the sampled hospitals, the survey will not be able to provide information about the prevalence of all antibiotic-resistant HAIs that occur in U.S. acute care hospitals. A further limitation is that the sample is not representative of U.S. acute care hospitals. As described earlier, this is because the survey is based on a sample of acute care hospitals located within the EIP surveillance areas, according to CDC officials.

CDC also plans to enhance its monitoring of HAIs by expanding the geographic coverage of its surveillance of *Clostridium difficile* infections and CDC officials told us that the agency is piloting additional surveillance for gram-negative infections through the EIP network.[92] According to CDC, the agency began monitoring *Clostridium difficile* infections through EIP in 2009 in 7 surveillance areas, to obtain more comprehensive and representative information about this infection, including for antibiotic resistance.[93] CDC officials stated that the agency plans to expand its *Clostridium difficile* monitoring to 10 surveillance areas by summer 2011. In 2 of the 10 surveillance areas (i.e., Oregon and Minnesota), surveillance will occur in rural areas only. CDC officials stated that the data will allow the agency, among other things, to detect *Clostridium difficile* infections that occur prior to admission to a healthcare facility and to identify new populations at risk.[94] CDC officials also told us that the agency is piloting surveillance for gram-negative infections that are resistant to multiple antibiotics, through the EIP network, as an exploratory effort and feasibility study on how to improve the agency's monitoring of these infections in healthcare settings.

In addition, CDC anticipates that the number of acute care hospitals participating in NHSN will expand in 2011 stemming from the CMS Hospital Inpatient Quality Reporting Program obligation to do so. The expanded participation will, CDC officials believe, result in more representative data about certain HAIs and antibiotic-resistant infections.[95] CMS has expanded its quality data measures to include two HAI measures that will be reported through NHSN. As stated previously, as of January 1, 2011, hospitals are obligated to report on central-line bloodstream infections associated with certain procedures from their intensive care units and on January 1, 2012, hospitals will be obligated to report on surgical site infections.[96] Hospitals will also need to report on antibiotic resistance associated with these two types of infections, given NHSN's reporting requirements for participation. As part of CDC's protocols, facilities submit microbiological data for each HAI identified, which includes the type of bacteria causing the infection and test results regarding antibiotic resistance.

Federal Agencies Do Not Monitor Antibiotic Disposal, But Have Examined the Presence of Antibiotics in the Environment, and Studies Find That Such Antibiotics Can Increase the Population of Resistant Bacteria

Federal agencies do not collect data regarding the disposal of most antibiotics intended for human use, but EPA and USGS have measured the presence of certain antibiotics in the environment due, in part, to their disposal. Studies conducted by scientists have found that antibiotics that are present in the environment at certain concentration levels can increase the population of resistant bacteria due to selective pressure.

Federal Agencies Do Not Monitor the Disposal of Most Antibiotics Intended for Human Use, but Have Measured the Presence of Antibiotics in the Environment

EPA does not monitor the disposal of most antibiotics intended for human use, but EPA and USGS have measured the presence of antibiotics in the environment, including water, soil, and sediment.[97] According to EPA, antibiotics enter the environment through various pathways into water, soil, and sediment, such as wastewater discharged from treatment plants.[98] The disposal of hazardous waste, such as chemicals that are harmful to human health when ingested, is regulated by EPA. Under RCRA, EPA has established a system by which hazardous waste is regulated from the time it is produced until it is disposed.[99] Under this system, EPA receives information from hazardous waste generators through the Biennial Reporting System.[100] EPA officials told us that antibiotics in general do not fall under RCRA's definition of hazardous waste; as a result, EPA does not generally receive information about the disposal of antibiotics. EPA officials further stated that the agency would receive limited information about antibiotics if they fell under RCRA's definition of hazardous waste. However, in part because it is the responsibility of the person disposing of a waste to determine whether or not it is hazardous, agency officials could not identify any specific antibiotics that fall under EPA's regulatory definition of hazardous waste and therefore concluded that it would be a rare occurrence for the agency to receive information on the disposal of antibiotics.

Under SDWA, EPA is authorized to regulate contaminants in public drinking water systems. EPA generally requires public water systems to monitor certain contaminants for which there are national primary drinking water regulations—standards limiting the concentration of a contaminant or requiring certain treatment. EPA has not promulgated any drinking water regulation for an antibiotic. EPA is required to identify and publish a list every 5 years of unregulated contaminants that may require regulation, known as the Contaminant Candidate List (CCL). EPA generally uses this list to select contaminants for its periodic regulatory determinations, by which the agency decides whether to regulate a contaminant, but contaminants may remain on the CCL for many years before EPA makes such a decision.[101] Erythromycin is the only antibiotic on the third CCL list (CCL 3)—the current CCL that was published in October 2009.[102] According to EPA officials, the agency is in the process of evaluating CCL 3 contaminants, including erythromycin, and plans to determine whether or not regulation is required for at least five contaminants from the CCL 3 by 2013. EPA's determination to promulgate a national primary drinking water regulation for a contaminant is made based on three criteria established under SDWA, including that the contaminant may have an adverse effect on human health.[103] To provide information such as that needed to determine whether to regulate the contaminant, EPA has the authority to require a subset of public water systems to monitor a limited number of unregulated contaminants, which the agency has implemented through the Unregulated Contaminant Monitoring Rule (UCMR). On March 3, 2011, EPA proposed the list of contaminants (primarily from the CCL 3) to be monitored under the third UCMR (UCMR 3). Erythromycin was not included on the proposed UCMR 3 list of contaminants, because according to EPA officials, further development of an analytical method that can be used for national monitoring of erythromycin is needed. EPA officials stated that the agency is in the initial stages of development of an analytical method for a number of pharmaceuticals, including erythromycin, and will evaluate the readiness of this analytical method for future UCMR efforts. EPA officials further stated that the agency will continue to evaluate unregulated contaminants, such as erythromycin, for future CCLs and will utilize any new data that become available.[104]

EPA and USGS have conducted several studies to measure the presence of antibiotics in the environment, which results partly from their disposal. According to EPA and USGS officials, there is no specific statutory mandate requiring the agencies to collect information about the presence of antibiotics in the environment. However, from 1999 through 2007, the agencies conducted five national studies measuring the presence and concentration of certain antibiotics in streams, groundwater, untreated drinking water, sewage sludge, and wastewater effluent as part of their efforts to study emerging contaminants.[105,106] (See table 5.) These studies were generally designed to determine whether certain contaminants, including antibiotics, were entering the environment and as a result, some study sites were selected based on being susceptible to contamination.[107] For example, the study examining the presence of antibiotics, and other contaminants, in streams in 30 states was designed to determine whether these contaminants were entering the environment. Therefore, USGS purposely selected study sites susceptible to contamination by humans, industry, and agricultural wastewater.

In all five studies antibiotics were found to be present. For example, erythromycin was detected in multiple samples tested in four studies and ciprofloxacin was detected in three studies.[108] According to EPA and USGS officials, the antibiotic concentrations detected in streams, groundwater, and untreated drinking water are low relative to the maximum recommended therapeutic doses approved by FDA for most antibiotics. In contrast, antibiotics were found in relatively higher concentrations in sewage sludge. For example, the maximum concentration level of ciprofloxacin that was detected in streams or untreated drinking water sources was .03 micrograms per liter of water.[109] In comparison, ciprofloxacin was detected in sewage sludge sampled from large publicly owned treatment plants at concentrations ranging from 74.5 to 47,000 micrograms per kilogram of sewage sludge.[110] The maximum recommended therapeutic dose for ciprofloxacin is about 13,000 micrograms per kilogram of weight. According to USGS officials, waste from humans and domestic animals that receive antibiotics (i.e., therapeutic or subtherapeutic doses) are likely to contain antibiotics as a substantial portion of such antibiotic treatments are not fully absorbed through the body.[111]

Table 5. Five National Studies that Measured the Presence of Antibiotics in the Environment, Conducted by EPA and USGS

`	Year(s) study was conducted	Description of study sites	Examples of antibiotics detected[a]
Pharmaceuticals, Hormones, and Other Organic Wastewater Contaminants in U.S. Streams, 1999-2000: A National Reconnaissance (USGS)	1999-2000	139 streams across 30 states.	Ciprofloxacin, Erythromycin, Tetracycline
A National Reconnaissance of Pharmaceuticals and Other Organic Wastewater Contaminants in the United States – I) Groundwater (USGS)	2000	47 groundwater sites across 18 states	Lincomycin, Sulfamethazine, Sulfamethoxazole
A National Reconnaissance for Pharmaceuticals and Other Organic Wastewater Contaminants in the United States – II) Untreated Drinking Water Sources (USGS)	2001	25 ground- and 49 surface-water sources of drinking water in 25 states and Puerto Rico.	Azithromycin, Ciprofloxacin, Erythromycin
Targeted National Sewage Sludge Survey (EPA)	2006-2007	74 publicly owned plants that treat wastewater in 35 states.	Azithromycin, Ciprofloxacin, Erythromycin
Transport of Chemicals from Wastewater Effluents (EPA and USGS)	2002	10 wastewater treatment plants in 10 states.	Erythromycin, Sulfamethoxazole, Trimethoprim

Source: GAO analysis and summary of EPA and USGS information.

[a] Detected antibiotics include those used for treatment by both animals and humans.

EPA and USGS also have two ongoing studies that measure the presence of antibiotics in wastewater and drinking water. First, EPA is assessing the concentration of pharmaceuticals and other contaminants in municipal wastewater because past studies have suggested that municipal wastewater is a likely source of human pharmaceuticals entering the environment.

According to EPA officials, EPA is collecting samples from 50 of the largest municipal wastewater plants in the United States and testing their treated effluents for contaminants, including 12 antibiotics.[112]

The study's findings are expected to be made available sometime in 2012 and may help EPA develop new standards for municipal wastewater treatment, according to EPA officials. Second, EPA and USGS are collaborating on a study to measure the presence of several antibiotics (e.g., erythromycin) and other contaminants in raw and finished drinking water to better determine human exposures to these contaminants through drinking water.[113] During 2011, researchers will take samples from between 20 and 25 drinking water treatment plants across the United States and according to EPA officials, the information will be used to inform EPA decision making about the focus of future monitoring efforts. EPA and USGS officials anticipate the study's findings to be made available sometime in 2012.

Studies Find Antibiotics Present in the Environment at Certain Concentration Levels Can Increase the Population of Resistant Bacteria Due to Selective Pressure

Scientific evidence gathered in our literature review shows that, at certain concentration levels, antibiotics present in the environment—in water and soil—can increase the population of resistant bacteria, due to selective pressure. Of the 15 studies we identified that examined this association, 5 examined water-related environments and 10 examined soil-related environments. Among these 15 studies, 11 provided evidence to support the association. Support for this association means that antibiotics present in these environments increased the population of resistant bacteria through selective pressure because bacteria containing resistance genes survived and multiplied.[114]

Results for the five studies examining water-related environments generally support an association between the presence of antibiotics and an increase in the population of resistant bacteria caused by selective pressure, although only one tested concentration levels of antibiotics as low as those that have been detected in national studies of U.S. streams, groundwater, and source drinking water. The results of this study were inconclusive as to whether low antibiotic concentration levels, such as levels measured at or below 1.7 micrograms per liter of water, led to an increase in the population of resistant bacteria.[115] Among the four other studies that supported an association between the presence of antibiotics and an increase in the population of resistant bacteria, the lowest concentration level associated with an increase was 20 micrograms of oxytetracycline per liter of water—over 50 times higher than maximum antibiotic concentration levels detected in stream water across the United States.[116] Another of these four studies found that chlortetracycline was associated with an increase in the population of resistant bacteria, but only at concentration levels over 1000 times higher than those that have been detected in streams across the United States.[117] According to USGS officials, scientists generally agree that the population of resistant bacteria would increase in water if the concentration levels of antibiotics that are present were to reach the minimum level that is known to induce antibiotic resistance in a clinical setting.[118,119] USGS officials further stated that higher concentrations of antibiotics have been found, for example, in waters near to pharmaceutical manufacturing facilities in countries outside of the United States.[120]

Results for the 10 studies examining antibiotic resistance in soil-related environments, such as soil and sediment, were more mixed, and we cannot draw comparisons between concentration levels tested in these studies and those that have been found in such environments across the United States. Seven of the 10 studies found evidence to support an association between the presence of antibiotics and an increase in the population of resistant bacteria due to selective pressure, and the association existed at all concentration levels studied. No association existed among the antibiotic concentration levels in the other 3 studies. Because national data about the presence and concentration levels of antibiotics in soil and sediment are not available, we cannot draw comparisons between concentration levels tested in these studies and those commonly found in such environments across the United States. As with water-related environments, USGS officials stated that scientists generally agree that the population of resistant bacteria would increase in soil if the concentration levels of antibiotics that are present were to reach the minimum level that is known to induce antibiotic resistance in clinical settings. USGS officials further stated that antibiotic concentration levels in soils where human and animal waste have been applied as fertilizer are likely to be directly related to the antibiotic concentration levels in these sources.[121]

CONCLUSIONS

Antibiotics have been widely prescribed to treat bacterial infections in humans and their use contributes to the development of antibiotic resistance, which is an increasing public health problem in the United States and worldwide. Monitoring the use of antibiotics in humans and preventing their inappropriate use, such as prescribing an antibiotic to treat a viral infection, is critically important because the use of antibiotics for any reason contributes to the development and spread of antibiotic resistance. Establishing patterns of antibiotic use is necessary for understanding current—and predicting future—patterns of antibiotic resistance. Monitoring overall antibiotic use in humans, including in inpatient and outpatient healthcare settings, is also needed to evaluate the contribution of such use—relative to other causes, such as animal use—to the overall problem of antibiotic resistance. Such information could help policymakers set priorities for actions to control the spread of antibiotic resistance.

CDC is collecting data on antibiotic use and the occurrence of resistance, but the agency's data sources have limited ability to provide accurate national estimates and do not allow it to assess associations between use and resistance. CDC does not monitor the use of antibiotics in inpatient settings—where antibiotic use is often intensive and prolonged and thus, the risk of antibiotic resistance is greater—although the agency believes such information would help it target and evaluate its own prevention efforts to reduce the occurrence of resistance. Although the agency collects annual data in the United States about the use of antibiotics in outpatient settings, the data do not allow CDC to assess geographic patterns of use in those settings. Similarly, CDC's monitoring of antibiotic-resistant infections does not allow the agency to assess the overall problem of antibiotic resistance because of gaps in the data it collects. Without more comprehensive information about the occurrence of cases of antibiotic-resistant infections and the use of antibiotics, the agency's ability to understand the overall scope of the public health problem, detect emerging trends, and plan and implement prevention activities is impeded. Further, the lack of comprehensive information about antibiotic-resistant infections and antibiotic use, and the most effective ways to reduce inappropriate prescribing, impedes CDC's ability to strategically target its resources directed at reducing the occurrence of antibiotic-resistant infections.

CDC is attempting to address the gaps in its data on antibiotic use in humans and on antibiotic-resistant infections by obtaining additional data, but it is not clear whether the steps it is taking will result in more comprehensive information from which the agency could assess the public health impact of antibiotic resistance. Further, it is not clear whether these steps will provide CDC with the information it needs to identify what actions are needed to reduce the occurrence of antibiotic-resistant infections.

RECOMMENDATIONS

To better prevent and control the spread of antibiotic resistance, we recommend that the Director of CDC take the following two actions:

- Develop and implement a strategy to improve CDC's monitoring of antibiotic use in humans, for example, by identifying available sources of antibiotic use information; and
- develop and implement a strategy to improve CDC's monitoring of antibiotic-resistant infections in inpatient healthcare facilities to more accurately estimate the national occurrence of such infections.

AGENCY COMMENTS

We provided a draft of this report for review to HHS, EPA, and DOI. HHS provided written comments, which are reproduced in appendix V. HHS, EPA, and DOI provided technical comments, which we incorporated as appropriate.

In its written comments, HHS generally agreed with the actions we recommend it take to improve its monitoring of antibiotic use and resistance. HHS says that steps are being taken to address existing gaps in CDC's monitoring of antibiotic use and the occurrence of antibiotic-resistant infections, and HHS noted that such monitoring is critically important in preventing the development and spread of antibiotic resistance. HHS highlighted examples of the steps CDC is taking, or plans to undertake, to address gaps in CDC's monitoring of antibiotic use and antibiotic-resistant infections, such as a planned survey of acute care hospitals in the United States. HHS noted that other planned activities to improve the monitoring of antibiotic use and antibiotic-resistant infections are described in the revised draft Action Plan, developed by the Interagency Task Force on Antimicrobial Resistance. HHS stated that CDC believes that the successful, timely accomplishment of its planned and ongoing activities to improve monitoring will result in information that is sufficiently comprehensive for a full and complete assessment of the public health impact of antibiotic resistance, and that this assessment will provide federal agencies with appropriate information to identify necessary actions to reduce the occurrence of antibiotic-resistant infections. HHS stated that it would provide updates on its progress toward the accomplishment of its steps to improve monitoring in the 2010 annual progress report on the Action Plan, scheduled for public release this summer. HHS also commented that it has initiated the process of developing a strategic plan for preventing the emergence and spread of antibiotic-resistant infections,and a primary component of this strategic plan is the monitoring of antibiotic use and resistance. We support this effort and encourage HHS, as it develops its strategic plan, to continue to examine approaches for improving its monitoring of antibiotic use and antibiotic-resistant infections that will help provide the agency with information that is needed to more accurately estimate the national occurrence of antibiotic-resistant infections.

As agreed with your offices, unless you publicly announce the contents of this report earlier, we plan no further distribution until 30 days from the report date. At that time, we will send copies to the Secretaries of the Department of Health and Human Services and the Department of the Interior, the Administrator of the Environmental Protection Agency, and other interested parties. In addition, the report will be available at no charge on the GAO Web site at http://www.gao.gov.

Marcia Crosse
Director, Health Care

APPENDIX I: METHODOLOGY FOR REVIEWING SCIENTIFIC EVIDENCE ON ANTIBIOTIC RESISTANCE IN THE ENVIRONMENT

To describe the scientific evidence on the development of antibiotic-resistant bacteria in the environment, we conducted a literature review. We identified literature made available since 2007 that reported scientific findings on antibiotic concentrations that induce bacteria located in the environment to become resistant as well as the ability of bacteria to spread resistance. We conducted a key word search of 39 databases, such as Elsevier Biobase and MEDLINE that included peer-reviewed journals and other periodicals to capture articles published on or between

January 1, 2007, and July 8, 2010. We searched these databases for articles with key words in their title or abstract related to both antibiotic resistance and the environment, such as combinations and variations of the words "resistance," "antibiotic," and "environment," and descriptive words for different environmental settings, such as "water," "sediment," "soil," and "sewage."[1] From these sources, we identified 241 articles, publications, and reports (which we call articles) published from January 1, 2007, through July 8, 2010. Of these 241 articles, we then excluded articles that (1) were not published in English, (2) were available only in an abstract form or in books or book chapters, (3) were not peer-reviewed, (4) contained only a review of past literature, or (5) were unrelated to antibiotic resistance found in the environment such as articles that focused on the effects of antibiotic resistance found mainly in clinical settings.[2] In total, we included 105 articles in our literature review. We supplemented the scientific findings analyzed in our literature review with contextual and background information gathered from articles that were identified as a result of our interviews with officials from the Environmental Protection Agency and the United States Geological Survey.

Appendix II: Bacteria and the Development of Antibiotic Resistance

Bacteria are single-celled organisms that live in water, soil, and in the bodies of humans, animals, and plants. Bacteria compete with each other for resources, such as nutrients, oxygen, and space, and those that do not compete successfully will not survive. Most bacteria that are present in humans, such as those found on the skin and in the intestines, are harmless because of the protective effects of the human immune system, and a few bacteria are beneficial. However, some bacteria are capable of causing disease. For example, *Escherichia coli* O157—which can be found in the feces of animals, such as cattle, and can transfer to people through contaminated undercooked meat—produce a toxin that causes severe stomach and bowel disorders, and death in some cases.[1] In addition, the same bacteria that may cause disease in one individual may not cause disease in another.[2] For example, *Streptococcus pneumoniae* is a bacterium that is often found in the noses and throats of healthy persons without causing disease, but it can also cause mild illness, such as sinus infections, as well as life-threatening infections such as meningitis. Furthermore, when the immune system is weakened, infection may be caused by certain bacteria that would not generally result in an infection in a healthy human.

Like other living things, as bacteria grow and multiply, they also evolve and adapt to changes in their surroundings. Bacteria adapt to their surroundings through selective pressure, which is created by, among other things, the presence of antibiotics.[3] Selective pressure means that when an antibiotic is introduced into a bacterial environment, some bacteria will be killed by the antibiotic while other bacteria will survive.[4] Bacteria are able to survive because they have certain genetic material that is coded for resistance—allowing them to avoid the effects of the antibiotic. The surviving bacteria that are resistant to antibiotics will multiply and quickly become the dominant bacterial type. Bacteria that are susceptible to the effects of antibiotics may become resistant to such antibiotics after acquiring resistant genetic material from bacteria that are resistant through horizontal gene transfer. Horizontal gene transfer is the movement of genetic material between bacteria, and can occur within a species of bacteria and can sometimes occur between certain species of bacteria.[5] Close proximity between bacteria, which allows certain genetic material to be shared, can facilitate gene transfer.

The movement of antibiotic-resistant bacteria around the world is accelerated because of international travel and global trade. Individuals can contract bacterial strains—that is, distinct types of bacteria—that are resistant to antibiotics abroad during travel, whether as active infections or as unaffected carriers, and then spread such strains to others at home.[6] The bacterial strains in different parts of the world may also contain different resistance genes than bacterial strains found domestically. For example, in 2010, the Centers for Disease Control and Prevention reported that three bacterial strains included a resistance gene identified for the first time in the United States. The emergence of the resistance gene was traced to patients who had received recent medical care in India.[7] Further, international trade of food and livestock may accelerate the movement of antibiotic-resistant bacteria because food and livestock also carry resistant bacterial strains that can be contracted by humans through consumption.

To determine whether bacteria are resistant, tests are performed that measure the susceptibility of pathogenic bacteria to particular antibiotics. The test results can predict the success or failure of an antibiotic treatment, and thus, guide healthcare providers' choice of antibiotics to treat bacterial infections. The test results include a numeric value, which is then interpreted according to established ranges.[8] For example, a value may be categorized as 'resistant,' meaning that the pathogenic bacterium is not inhibited by the concentration of the antibiotic that usually results in growth inhibition.[9]

Appendix III: Centers for Disease Control and Prevention's Surveillance Systems for Monitoring Antibiotic Resistance

Table 6. CDC's Surveillance Systems for Monitoring Antibiotic Resistance, by Bacteria, Geographic Coverage, and Examples of Data Use

Surveillance system	Bacteria monitored for antibiotic resistance	Geographic coverage of surveillance	Examples of how surveillance data were used
Active Bacterial Core Surveillance (ABCs) [of the Emerging Infections Programs (EIP) Network[a]]	group A and group B Strepto-coccus; Neisseria meningitidis; Strepto-coccus pneumoniae; methicillin-resistant Staphylo-coccus aureus (MRSA)[b]	10 surveillance areas in California, Colorado, Connecticut, Georgia, Maryland, Minnesota, New Mexico, New York, Oregon, and Tennessee for group A and B Streptococcus; Neisseria meningitidis; and Streptococcus pneumoniae 9 surveillance areas in California, Colorado, Connecticut, Georgia, Maryland, Minnesota, New York, Oregon, and Tennessee for MRSA	ABCs data were used to show that rates of invasive pneumococcal infections, including antibiotic-resistant infections among children and adults, have declined since a pneumococcal conjugate vaccine was introduced for children in 2000. ABCs data have also shown a decline in the incidence of pneumococcal meningitis resistant to antibiotics. ABCs data on MRSA, collected between 2005 and 2008, were used to identify the genetic makeup of MRSA strains showing unusual patterns of resistance. This information provided the Centers for Disease Control and Prevention (CDC) with evidence that mechanisms of resistance in MRSA were being transferred from healthcare-associated to community-associated strains.

Surveillance system	Bacteria monitored for antibiotic resistance	Geographic coverage of surveillance	Examples of how surveillance data were used
Gonococcal Isolate Surveillance Project (GISP)	Neisseria gonorrhoeae	29 sexually transmitted disease clinics located in the West, Midwest, Northeast, and South	Based on GISP data, CDC announced in 2007 that fluoroquinolones were no longer recommended to treat gonorrhea because of antibiotic resistance and that the recommended treatment for gonorrhea was limited to only cephalosporin antibiotics. Neisseria gonorrhoeae isolates collected through GISP have been used to support research on the mechanisms used to resist the effects of antibiotics, according to a CDC official
National Antimicrobial Resistance Monitoring System: Enteric Bacteria (NARMS: EB)	Shigella, Escherichia coli O157, Campylobacter, typhoidal Salmonella, and non-typhoidal Salmonella[c]	50 states for Shigella, typhoidal Salmonella, non-typhoidal Salmonella, and Escherichia coli O157 10 states for Campylobacter — California, Colorado, Connecticut, Georgia, Maryland, Minnesota, New Mexico, New York, Oregon, and Tennessee	NARMS: EB data were used in 2005 to support the Food and Drug Administration's (FDA) withdrawal of approval for the use of enrofloxacin in chickens and turkeys. Enrofloxacin, a fluoroquinolone, marketed under the trade name Baytril, had been approved for use in poultry production. In September 2005, FDA withdrew its approval because of concerns about the spread of fluoroquinolone-resistant Campylobacter from poultry to humans. NARMS: EB data from 1996-2006 were used to identify mechanisms of resistance to cephalosporins among specific types of Salmonella.

Table 6. (Continued)

Surveillance system	Bacteria monitored for antibiotic resistance	Geographic coverage of surveillance	Examples of how surveillance data were used
National Healthcare Safety Network (NHSN)	Includes, among others, Enterococcus faecalis; Enterococcus faecium; Staphylococcus aureus; Acinetobacter; Escherichia coli; Enterobacter; Klebsiella oxytoca; Klebsiella pneumoniae; Pseudomonas aeruginosa; and Clostridium difficile	Participating healthcare facilities across the United States	Participating facilities have used NHSN data to assess their own healthcare-associated infection (HAI) rates, by comparing their rates with national rates.CDC also compiled 2006-2007 data on antibiotic resistance across participating facilities and reported, for example, that as many as 16 percent of all HAIs observed in NHSN were associated with nine multidrug-resistant bacteria, such as MRSA.
National Notifiable Diseases Surveillance System (NNDSS)	Streptococcus pneumoniae	Health departments in the 50 states, 5 territories, New York City, and the District of Columbia voluntarily report cases to CDC	CDC has determined that NNDSS data are likely to be used to assess the impact of a vaccine that was approved in 2010 to prevent additional strains of Streptococcus pneumoniae.

Surveillance system	Bacteria monitored for antibiotic resistance	Geographic coverage of surveillance	Examples of how surveillance data were used
National Tuberculosis Surveillance System(NTSS)	Mycobacterium tuberculosis	CDC receives information on each newly reported case of tuberculosis (TB) in the United States.	In 2010, after expanding the NTSS data collection with the TB Genotyping Information Management System, CDC officials used genotypes identified with the system to assist an investigation of a TB outbreak among healthcare workers. As a result of the investigation, the probable source for the TB outbreak was identified.

Source: GAO analysis and summary of CDC information.

[a] Since 2009, CDC has monitored Clostridium difficile infections in healthcare and community settings through EIP (as part of its Healthcare Associated Infections Surveillance). CDC officials stated that these data complement the Clostridium difficile data that are captured through the National Healthcare Safety Network and will, among other things, inform vaccine development.

[b] Haemophilus influenzae are monitored for antibiotic resistance periodically.

[c] According to CDC officials, NARMS: EB collects data on Enterococci from 2 states and has a pilot study to monitor Escherichia coli in 1 state.

Appendix IV: Topical Antiseptics and Antibiotic Resistance

Topical antiseptics are products that are used to reduce the risk of infection by killing or inhibiting the growth of microorganisms, such as bacteria, on the skin. Topical antiseptic products are diverse, and include those targeted for healthcare settings, such as surgical hand scrubs and patient preoperative skin preparations; products targeted to consumers for general body cleansing include antibacterial soaps; and products specifically intended for use by food handlers. Topical antiseptics contain a variety of active ingredients; for example, triclosan and triclocarban are commonly used in antibacterial liquid and bar soaps, while alcohol is used in leave-on handwashes.[1] Because antiseptics are intended for use in or on humans or animals,[2] they are considered drugs and are approved and regulated as nonprescription drugs by the Food and Drug Administration (FDA) under the Federal Food, Drug, and Cosmetic Act.[3] There are concerns by public officials, and others, about the possibility that the use of, or exposure to, topical antiseptics causes antibiotic resistance in bacteria. This process is called cross-resistance.[4]

FDA has conducted a review of the scientific literature regarding the relationship between exposure to active ingredients in topical antiseptics—including triclosan or triclocarban—and cross-resistance. According to the available scientific evidence that FDA has reviewed, bacteria are able to develop resistance to both antiseptics and antibiotics in the laboratory setting, but the relationship outside of the laboratory setting is not clear. For example, a laboratory study has shown that when certain strains of the bacteria *Escherichia coli* (E. coli) are exposed to triclosan, the E. coli not only acquire a high level of resistance to triclosan, but also demonstrate cross-resistance to various antibiotics, such as erythromycin and tetracycline.[5] However, a study that examined household use of certain antiseptic products did not show an association between their use and the development of antibiotic resistance.[6] According to FDA, the possibility that bacteria can develop cross-resistance to antibiotics from exposure to antiseptics warrants further evaluation. FDA will seek additional data regarding the safety of topical antiseptic products, for example, on the effects of antiseptics on cross-resistance, when it issues a proposed rule to amend the current monograph for antiseptic drug products. FDA officials told us that they expect the proposed rule to be published for public comment sometime in 2011.

The Environmental Protection Agency (EPA) and the United States Geological Survey (USGS) conducted five national studies between 1999 and 2007 that measured for the presence of the antiseptic active ingredients triclosan and triclocarban in the environment.[7] These studies tested for the presence and concentration of the antiseptic active ingredients along with other contaminants including antibiotics, in streams, groundwater, untreated drinking water, sewage sludge, and wastewater effluent.[8] (See table 6.) Each of the studies measured for the presence of triclosan, and the study involving sewage sludge also tested for triclocarban.[9] Triclosan was found to be present in 94 percent of sewage sludge samples, 100 percent of wastewater effluent samples, and 57.6 percent of stream samples tested from sites across the United States.

Table 7. Five National Studies that Measured the Presence of Antiseptic Active Ingredients in the Environment, Conducted by EPA and USGS

Name of study (agency that conducted the study)	Year(s) study was conducted	Description of study sites	Examples of antiseptic active ingredients tested
Pharmaceuticals, Hormones, and Other Organic Wastewater Contaminants in U.S. Streams, 1999-2000: A National Reconnaissance (USGS)	1999-2000	139 streams across 30 states	Triclosan
A National Reconnaissance of Pharmaceuticals and Other Organic Wastewater Contaminants in the United States – I) Groundwater (USGS)	2000	47 groundwater sites across18 states	Triclosan
A National Reconnaissance for Pharmaceuticals and Other Organic Wastewater Contaminants in the United States – II) Untreated Drinking Water Sources (USGS)	2001	25 ground- and 49 surface-water sources of drinking water in 25 states and Puerto Rico	Triclosan
Targeted National Sewage Sludge Survey (EPA)	2006-2007	74 publicly owned plants that treat wastewater in 35 states	Triclosan and Triclocarban
Transport of Chemicals from Wastewater Effluents (EPA and USGS)	2002	10 wastewater treatment plants in10 states	Triclosan

Source: GAO analysis and summary of EPA and USGS information.

It was also detected in 14.9 percent of groundwater samples and 8.1 percent of untreated drinking water samples.[10] Triclocarban was found to be present in all sewage sludge samples taken from wastewater treatment plants located across the United States.[11]

APPENDIX V: COMMENTS FROM THE DEPARTMENT OF HEALTH AND HUMAN SERVICES

DEPARTMENT OF HEALTH & HUMAN SERVICES — OFFICE OF THE SECRETARY

Assistant Secretary for Legislation
Washington, DC 20201

MAY 13 2011

Marcia Crosse
Director, Health Care
U.S. Government Accountability Office
441 G Street N.W.
Washington, DC 20548

Dear Ms. Crosse:

Attached are comments on the U.S. Government Accountability Office's (GAO) draft report entitled, "ANTIBIOTIC RESISTANCE: Data Gaps Will Remain Despite HHS Taking Steps to Improve Monitoring" (GAO-11-406).

The Department appreciates the opportunity to review this report before its publication.

Sincerely,

Jim R. Esquea
Assistant Secretary for Legislation

Attachment

GENERAL COMMENTS OF THE DEPARTMENT OF HEALTH AND HUMAN SERVICES (HHS) ON THE GOVERNMENT ACCOUNTABILITY OFFICE'S (GAO) DRAFT REPORT ENTITLED, "ANTIBIOTIC RESISTANCE: DATA GAPS WILL REMAIN DESPITE HHS TAKING STEPS TO IMPROVE MONITORING" (GAO 11-406)

The Department appreciates the opportunity to review and comment on this draft report.

The Centers for Disease Control and Prevention (CDC) agrees with the GAO that monitoring and surveillance of antimicrobial use and the occurrence of resistant infections are critically important in preventing the development and spread of antibiotic resistance.

As GAO notes, CDC has previously recognized gaps in the monitoring and surveillance of antimicrobial use and resistance and is taking specific steps to address these gaps. As noted in the report, these steps include:

- The planned prevalence survey of U.S. acute care hospitals
- Addition of the antimicrobial use and resistance module to NHSN
- Increase in sample size of the National Ambulatory Medical Care Survey
- Acquisition of antimicrobial use data from private vendors
- Sharing of data among Federal agencies, including FDA, NIH and CMS, which is expanding its own data collections in collaboration with CDC's NHSN
- Continued growth of the NHSN and the enhancement of components which collect data from outpatient facilities

Additional CDC activities, not specifically mentioned in the GAO report, are described in the draft document A Public Health Action Plan to Combat Antimicrobial Resistance produced by the Interagency Task Force on Antimicrobial Resistance (http://www.cdc.gov/drugresistance/pdf/2010/Interagency-Action-Plan-PreClearance-03-2011.pdf). This document identifies over 50 specific actions being undertaken by Task Force members to improve monitoring and surveillance of antimicrobial use and resistant infections; for the majority of these actions, CDC is the lead agency. Among these actions are:

- Enhancements to the National Antimicrobial Monitoring System
- Enhancements to the Gonococcal Isolate Surveillance Project
- Enhancements to antimicrobial resistance monitoring conducted through the Emerging Infections Program
- Enhancements to the Active Bacterial Core Surveillance system
- Enhancements to the national tuberculosis reporting system
- Collaborations with non-Federal public health agencies (state and local health departments, the Conference of State and Territorial Epidemiologists, the Association of Public Health Laboratories), non-governmental organizations (e.g., the Clinical and Laboratory Standards Institute), and international organizations (e.g., World Health Organization) to improve monitoring and surveillance of antimicrobial resistance

GENERAL COMMENTS OF THE DEPARTMENT OF HEALTH AND HUMAN SERVICES (HHS) ON THE GOVERNMENT ACCOUNTABILITY OFFICE'S (GAO) DRAFT REPORT ENTITLED, "ANTIBIOTIC RESISTANCE: DATA GAPS WILL REMAIN DESPITE HHS TAKING STEPS TO IMPROVE MONITORING" (GAO 11-406)

Updates on CDC's progress toward successful accomplishment of these action steps will be further documented in the 2010 annual progress report on the Action Plan, scheduled for release this summer.

CDC believes that the successful, timely accomplishment of the numerous action steps currently in process and planned by CDC and in collaboration with Federal and non-Federal partners will result in the Federal agencies having sufficiently comprehensive information for a full and complete assessment of the public health impact of antibiotic resistance and will provide Federal agencies with appropriate information to identify necessary actions to reduce the occurrence of antibiotic-resistant infections.

Finally, CDC has initiated the process of developing a strategic plan for preventing the emergence and spread of antimicrobial resistant infections, of which a primary component is the monitoring and surveillance of antimicrobial use and resistance.

End Notes

[1] For example, the medical costs attributable to the treatment of an antibiotic-resistant infection ranged from about $19,000 to $29,000 per patient in a study of one hospital. Inaddition, the excess duration of a hospital stay was about 6 to 13 days and the death rate was twofold higher among those patients who were treated for such infections. See R.R. Roberts et al., "Hospital and Societal Costs of Antimicrobial-Resistant Infections in a Chicago Teaching Hospital: Implications for Antibiotic Stewardship, *Clinical Infectious Diseases*, vol. 49 (2009), pp. 1175-1184.

[2] GAO has ongoing work examining antibiotic use in food animals.

[3] For example, a recent report from the American Academy of Microbiology outlined several recommendations to help control the development and spread of antibioticresistance, including improved surveillance to better assess the actual scope of the problem. See American Academy of Microbiology, *Antibiotic Resistance: An Ecological Perspective on an Old Problem* (Washington, D.C.: 2009).

[4] See House of Representatives, *Departments of Labor, Health, and Human Services, and Education, and Related Agencies Appropriations Bill, 2010: Report of the Committee on Appropriations together with Minority Views*, Report 111-220 (Washington, D.C.: July 22, 2009).

[5] The company IMS Health, on a monthly basis, collects data on drugs—including antibiotics—purchased by retail pharmacies from about 100 drug manufacturers and about 500 distribution centers. These manufacturers and distribution centers provide data to IMS Health on the number of units sold.

[6] The Red Book Advanced database includes a comprehensive list of drug products approved for use by the Food and Drug Administration.

[7] IMS Health conducts detailed data reliability assessments, which include comparing monthly data from drug manufacturers and distribution centers to data from the prior month and the prior year in order to ensure consistency.

[8] The Healthcare Infection Control Practices Advisory Committee is comprised of public infection control experts, as well as nonvoting federal agency representatives and nonvoting liaison representatives of several national organizations. The committee is charged with providing advice and guidance to the Secretary of HHS and the Centers for Disease Control and Prevention, among others, regarding the practice of healthcare infection control, strategies for surveillance, and prevention and control of healthcareassociated infections in U.S. healthcare facilities. The officials we interviewed from the three liaison organizations represented the Association of Professionals of Infection Control and Epidemiology, Inc., the Infectious Diseases Society of America, and the Society for Healthcare Epidemiology of America.

[9] PhRMA officials provided us information on how pharmaceutical manufacturers dispose of unused drugs, such as those that are expired or were recalled, and active ingredients that do not get used in the manufacturing process.

[10] Antibiotics are a type of antimicrobial. Antimicrobials are drugs or other chemicals that kill or slow the growth of organisms such as bacteria, viruses, and fungi.

[11] Diagnostic tests are used to determine the types of bacteria that cause infection and this information can be used by healthcare providers to choose an appropriate antibiotic. Different antibiotics target different types of bacteria.

[12] In addition, some communities conduct pharmaceutical take-back programs that allow the public to bring unused or expired drugs to a central location for disposal.

[13] The guidance, available on the FDA Web site, states that consumers should follow these guidelines unless the drug's label directs consumers to flush the unused drug down the toilet. FDA recommends flushing for a small number of drugs to prevent life-threatening risks from accidental use. See http://www.fda.gov/forconsumers/consumerupdates/ucm101653.htm, downloaded on March 31, 2011.

[14] Wastewater that leaves a treatment plant is known as effluent. Solid, semisolid, or liquid organic materials that leave a wastewater treatment plant are known as sewage sludge or biosolids. Sewage sludge is often applied to land as fertilizer, subject to EPA regulations.

[15] Inadequately treated sewage from such septic systems can be a cause of groundwater contamination.

[16] In general, a contaminant is any substance or matter in the environment such as those that have an adverse effect on air, water, soil, or human health.

[17] For a discussion of wastewater treatment plants and their ability to remove low concentrations of antibiotics, see J.R. Lefkowitz and M. Duran, "Changes in Antibiotic Resistance Patterns of *Escherichia coli* during Domestic Wastewater Treatment," *Water Environment Research*, vol. 81 (2009), pp. 878-885.

[18] Antibiotics can also enter sewage systems as a result of bathing and washing. Bathing and washing may release antibiotic ingredients remaining on the skin from the use of topical applications or from excretion to the skin through sweating.

[19] Antibiotics may also enter the environment as a result of their use in aquaculture and orchards (e.g., antibiotics may be sprayed on apple or pear trees to prevent certain infections).

[20] CDC officials told us that the act has been interpreted broadly to include CDC's surveillance of antibiotic-resistant infections and the use of antibiotics. See Public Health Service Act, as amended, § 301(a), codified at 42 U.S.C. § 241(a) (2011).

[21] The Public Health Improvement Act required that the Secretary of HHS establish the Task Force to provide advice and recommendations related to antibiotic resistance. Under the act, the secretary—in consultation with the Task Force and state and local public health officials—is required to develop, improve, coordinate, or enhance participation in a surveillance plan to detect and monitor emerging antibiotic resistance. The act also states that the secretary, in consultation with the Task Force and others, shall develop and implement educational programs for the general public to increase awareness of the appropriate use of antibiotics and to instruct healthcare professionals in the prudent use of antibiotics. See 42 U.S.C. § 247d-5 (2011).

[22] The Task Force includes eight other federal agency members. These members are the Agency for Healthcare Research and Quality, Centers for Medicare & Medicaid Services, Health Resources and Services Administration, HHS Office of the Assistant Secretary for Preparedness and Response, Department of Agriculture, Department of Defense, Department of Veterans Affairs, and EPA.

[23] The revised draft Action Plan includes the same focus areas—surveillance, prevention and control, research, and product development—as the 2001 Action Plan, along with specific projects or implementation steps for many of the action items. The revised draft Action Plan includes expected completion dates for projects or implementation steps, unlike the 2001 Action Plan.

[24] Hazardous waste has properties, such as being toxic, that make it dangerous or potentially harmful to human health or the environment.

[25] Surveillance systems include the timely dissemination of data to persons who can undertake effective prevention and control activities, such as public health personnel and clinicians.

[26] MRSA infections can also spread in the community, for example, by having close skin-toskin contact or by exposure to contaminated items and surfaces. ABCs monitors MRSA that is spread in the community as well as in healthcare settings.

[27] In contrast, FDA recently issued a report summarizing data on antibiotics sold or distributed for use in food-producing animals, as required by the Animal Drug User Fee Amendments of 2008. This report indicated that 28.7 million pounds of antibiotics were sold or distributed for use in food-producing animals in the United States in 2009. This number includes the antibiotic class ionophores, which are not used in human medicine. Excluding ionophores, the total amount of pounds of antibiotics that were sold or distributed for use in food-producing animals in the United States in 2009 was 20.5 million pounds. According to FDA, these data are limited because they combine therapeutic and subtherapeutic uses of antibiotics and all species of animals. Further, these data do not take into account the dose size, which varies by individual antibiotic and species of animal, or the total number of animals that received antibiotics. Due to such limitations in the data, FDA officials noted that comparisons of antibiotic use between food-producing animals and humans are problematic. See FDA, *2009 Summary Report on Antimicrobials Sold or Distributed for Use in Food-Producing Animals* (Rockville, Md: 2010). Available at http://www.fda.gov/ downloads/ForIndustry/ UserFees/AnimalDrugUserFeeActADUFA/UCM 231851.pdf.

28 NDAs and ANDAs are submitted to FDA by drug sponsors to obtain approval for their drug to be marketed in the United States.

[29] 21 C.F.R. §§ 314.81(b)(2)(ii)(a), 314.98(c) (2011). Generally, only aggregated drug distribution data can be made publicly available. 21 C.F.R. § 314.430(g)(2) (2011).

[30] In April 2011, in response to a request from a Member of Congress, FDA used drug sales data to provide information about the amount of antibiotics that were sold in the United States in 2009 for human use, which it provided in correspondence to the Member.

[31] The USITC data on antibiotic production reflected the amount of antibiotics that were produced—for human and animal use—in the United States and for sale within or outside of the United States. USITC began reporting on the production of antibiotics, and other organic chemicals at the request of the House Committee on Ways and Means. In 1995, the committee requested that USITC stop its data collection on production because it determined that this effort was no longer cost effective or essential for ensuring the competitiveness of the U.S. industry.

[32] A limitation of comparing total weights across antibiotic classes is that dosages for antibiotics can vary by antibiotic class. According to FDA officials, comparing weights within antibiotic class may also be difficult, but the degree to which antibiotic dosages may vary within the same class is less than that across classes.

[33] A drug is delivered to the body through oral administration when taken by mouth (e.g., a pill) and by injectable administration when delivered to the body through a needle.

[34] NAMCS and NHAMCS are national probability sample surveys that are designed to provide information about medical care services in the United States.

[35] The NAMCS sample does not include visits to office-based physicians who are employed by the federal government.

[36] The NHAMCS sample includes nonfederal short-stay hospitals (i.e., average stay of fewer than 30 days) whose specialty is general (i.e., medical or surgical) or children's general. The NHAMCS sample also includes ambulatory surgery centers that are freestanding. Ambulatory surgery centers are medical facilities where surgical and other procedures not requiring an overnight hospital stay are performed.

[37] According to CDC officials, CDC is planning to merge NHAMCS with its current survey on inpatient care (i.e., the National Hospital Discharge Survey), into one survey called the National Hospital Care Survey, in 2011. In the integrated survey, data collection for antibiotic prescriptions will continue for outpatient visits.

[38] The surveys do not collect information on whether the prescriptions were filled or whether the prescribed treatment course was completed by the patient. According to CDC officials, this is because individual patients in the surveys are never identified or contacted.

[39] Acute care hospitals provide inpatient medical care and other related services for surgery, acute medical conditions, or injuries, usually for a short-term illness or condition.

[40] Some antibiotics are used to prevent infections, such as prior to having certain kinds of surgery that carry a high risk of infection.

[41] CDC officials also stated that information about inpatient antibiotic use could inform recommendations about antibiotic treatment by professional groups, such as the Infectious Diseases Society of America.

[42] The survey is based on a sample of acute care hospitals located within the 10 EIP surveillance areas (also known as 'catchment' areas). According to a CDC official, the survey will be representative of hospitals within the EIP surveillance areas.

[43] CDC officials stated that a decision to repeat the survey will depend on available resources, and would be better made after the original survey has been completed. CDC expects to begin data collection in 2011 and complete its analysis in 2012.

[44] In NHSN, similar types of surveillance information are grouped into modules. For example, there is a module that captures surgical site infections.

[45] To illustrate, facilities reported on about 75 commonly used antibiotics as well as combinations of these antibiotics.

[46] CDC officials also told us that with the redesigned module, facilities will be able to immediately use their data to evaluate antibiotic use rates for antimicrobial stewardship

activities. Antimicrobial stewardship includes interventions and programs designed to improve antibiotic use.

[47] CDC officials stated that there are no plans to provide state-level estimates with NHAMCS.

[48] Otherwise healthy adults under 50 years old are an additional target audience.

[49] According to CDC officials, the program was originally named the National Campaign for Appropriate Antibiotic Use in the Community and was renamed Get Smart in 2003.

[50] In addition to health insurance companies, other Get Smart partners include businesses, pharmaceutical companies, foundations, and professional associations. As an example of how CDC collaborates with its partners, a health insurance company mailed Get Smart promotional materials to 320,000 of its customers with children ages 3 to 10 years old. CDC also provided technical support to this company to develop educational kits that were sent to about 30,000 pediatric, family practice, and internal medicine offices.

[51] In 2005, CDC launched two additional components of the national media campaign. These include materials for healthy adults, Spanish speakers, and American Indians. In 2008, the campaign coordinated its first national observance, Get Smart About Antibiotics Week, and through a variety of activities and resources, the messages of the Get Smart program were delivered to the public.

[52] Both measures are used by HHS, as part of Healthy People 2010, to assess national progress related to disease prevention.

[53] NCQA is a private organization whose mission is to improve healthcare quality. As part of its mission, NCQA develops quality standards and performance measures for a broad range of healthcare entities. The NCQA measures are used by more than 90 percent of U.S. health plans to measure performance. CDC officials helped NCQA write the measures on antibiotic prescribing.

[54] NCQA also measures the percentage of healthy adults (18 to 64 years of age) who did not receive an antibiotic prescription with a diagnosis of acute bronchitis, characterized by a cough that can last for up to 3 weeks. Performance on this measure declined between 2005 and 2008 because the percentage decreased.

[55] The American Academy of Pediatrics has recommended influenza vaccination for healthy children 6 through 24 months of age since 2004. Currently, the American Academy of Pediatrics recommends the influenza vaccination for healthy children 6 months of age and older.

[56] See J.A. Finkelstein et al., "Impact of a 16-Community Trial to Promote Judicious Antibiotic Use in Massachusetts," *Pediatrics*, vol. 121 (2008), pp. e15-e23.

[57] Antibiotic prescribing rates decreased in all three age groups of children included in the study, regardless of whether educational and promotional materials were distributed. For example, rates decreased by 14.5 percent among children 2 years old to less than 4 years old in communities with educational and promotional materials, and by 10.3 percent in communities without such materials. The greater declines in antibiotic prescribing rates in communities with educational and promotional materials were statistically significant in two of the three age groups.

[58] When a medication is first sold, the drug manufacturer has exclusive rights, or a patent, to produce that drug for a certain number of years. After the patent has expired, the drug becomes an off-patent medication and can be reproduced by other drug manufacturers.

[59] As of March 2011, this study is ongoing, according to an NIH official.

[60] As of March 2011, both studies are ongoing and continue to enroll participants, according to an NIH official.

[61] See C.C. Boehme et al., "Rapid Molecular Detection of Tuberculosis and Rifampin Resistance," *New England Journal of Medicine*, vol. 363, no. 1 (2010), pp. 1005-1015.

[62] The test is also being recommended for the early diagnosis of multidrug-resistant TB and TB in individuals infected with human immunodeficiency virus.

[63] As part of this effort, NIH has funded basic research, proof-of-concept studies, and preclinical research, according to an NIH official.

[64] This candidate is currently in the first phase of clinical testing, which is supported by a company. A multivalent staphylococcal vaccine would provide broader protection against a variety of *Staphylococcus aureus* strains.

[65] An NIH official further explained that the influenza virus causes lung damage that often predisposes individuals to bacterial pneumonia. Thus, fewer cases of influenza would lead to fewer secondary bacterial infections requiring antibiotic treatment.

[66] See 21 § CFR 201.24 (2011), 68 *Fed. Reg.* 6081 (Feb. 6, 2003). The amended drug labeling requirement applies only to antibiotics that are administered orally or intravenously. Antibiotics that are administered via a different route, such as those that are applied topically, are excluded from the labeling requirement.

[67] For FDA information related to antibiotic use, see http://www.fda.gov/NewsEvents/PublicHealthFocus/ucm235649.htm (downloaded on March 17, 2011).

[68] With laboratory-identified event surveillance data from NHSN, CDC also monitors certain HAIs caused by multidrug-resistant organisms (MDRO) as well as *Clostridium difficile* infections.

[69] Enrollment in NHSN is open to all types of healthcare facilities in the United States, including acute care hospitals, psychiatric hospitals, rehabilitation hospitals, outpatient dialysis centers, ambulatory surgery centers, and long-term-care facilities.

[70] CMS is the agency that, among other activities, administers Medicare, a health insurance program that helps pay for inpatient care in hospitals.

[71] CDC officials said that as of January 2011, approximately 4,000 hospitals and other healthcare facilities participated in NHSN. In comparison, we reported in 2008 that approximately 1,000 hospitals were participating in NHSN, as of December 2007. See GAO, *Health-Care-Associated Infections in Hospitals: Leadership Needed from HHS to Prioritize Prevention Practices and Improve Data on These Infections*, GAO-08-283 (Washington, D.C.: Mar. 31, 2008). NHSN opened enrollment to all types of healthcare facilities in 2008. According to the American Hospital Association's 2009 annual survey of hospitals, there are approximately 5,800 hospitals in the United States.

[72] The procedures include, for example, coronary artery bypass graft and other cardiac surgery, and hip or knee arthroplasty.

[73] Acute care hospitals electing to participate in the Hospital Inpatient Quality Reporting Program are obligated to report certain quality data measures to CMS; those that do not participate are penalized by a reduction in the increase they would otherwise receive to their annual payments for providing inpatient services to Medicare beneficiaries. Under the Hospital Inpatient Quality Reporting Program, NHSN was designated by CMS to serve as the reporting mechanism for certain HAIs.

[74] In 2008, we similarly stated that NHSN was limited in terms of its inability to produce reliable national estimates on the frequency of all HAIs—not just antibiotic-resistant HAIs. This is because NHSN data do not reflect the full scope of HAIs and the sample is not representative of facilities nationwide. See GAO-08-283.

[75] Facilities may report on different types of HAIs for which NHSN has developed detailed definitions and protocols. As part of the protocols, facilities submit microbiological data for

each HAI identified, provided by the facility's designated clinical microbiology laboratory. These data include information about the type of bacteria causing the infection and test results regarding antibiotic resistance. NHSN also has a protocol for reporting MDROs and *Clostridium difficile* infections as laboratory-identified events and, according to CDC officials, the test results regarding antibiotic resistance are used to determine whether such cases should be reported.

[76] Central line-associated bloodstream infections, catheter-associated urinary tract infections, and ventilator-associated pneumonia are device-associated infections that can be reported through NHSN. Surgical site infections and postprocedure pneumonia are procedure-associated infections that can also be reported. MDRO and *Clostridium difficile* infections can be reported into NHSN as HAIs or as laboratory-identified events.

[77] Laboratory-identified event surveillance data from NHSN also allow CDC to determine, among reported cases, the number of MDRO and *Clostridium difficile* infections.

[78] NARMS: EB also collects cases from the District of Columbia, and NTSS reporting includes the District of Columbia, Puerto Rico, and other U.S. jurisdictions in the Pacific and Caribbean.

7[9] NARMS: EB collects every case, every other case, or every fifth case of *Campylobacter* from each of the 10 state health departments, depending on the number of cases each health department receives.

[80] CDC also monitors *Haemophilus influenzae* with ABCs, but CDC officials stated that they do not routinely collect antibiotic susceptibility testing data for cases of *Haemophilus influenzae* infection, in part, because of constraints on time and resources at CDC's laboratories, but that the agency does conduct some testing for clusters of cases.

[81] CDC uses ABCs to monitor community- and healthcare-associated cases of MRSA. CDC also monitors healthcare-associated MRSA through NHSN.

[82] In addition to ABCs, CDC monitors cases of *Streptococcus pneumoniae* through NNDSS. CDC officials told us that NNDSS is used to monitor cases in areas not covered by ABCs' surveillance. NNDSS relies on the voluntary submission of case reports and it is considered a passive surveillance system. In comparison, ABCs is considered an active surveillance system because it relies on the active identification and collection of cases on a regular basis.

[83] The 10 states are California, Colorado, Connecticut, Georgia, Maryland, Minnesota, New Mexico, New York, Oregon, and Tennessee. CDC's surveillance of *Streptococcus pneumoniae, Neisseria meningitidis,* and group A and B *Streptococcus* is based on geographic areas located in these 10 states and surveillance of MRSA is based on geographic areas located in 9 of the 10 states.

[84] Bacterial isolates are sent to CDC and other laboratories for testing. CDC officials told us that antibiotic susceptibility testing is conducted on all cases of *Neisseria meningitidis, Streptococcus pneumoniae,* group A *Streptococcus,* and MRSA, as well as a subset of group B *Streptococcus* cases that are submitted to ABCs from 8 of the 10 sites.

[85] To illustrate the population sizes covered by ABCs surveillance, the population for *Neisseria meningitidis* surveillance is about 41 million and the population for MRSA surveillance is about 19 million, as of January 2010.

[86] CDC uses ABCs data to calculate national estimates of certain diseases, based on race and age information from ABCs surveillance areas and the 2009 U.S. population.

[87] CDC officials stated that the selection of catchment areas in urban areas allows the agency to capture a significant percentage of the population in the state.

[88] GISP surveillance collects information about gonorrhea cases from more locations in the West because CDC officials said they expect antibiotic resistance in gonorrhea to emerge first in the western United States and then to spread eastward.

[89] A CDC official told us that he does not believe there are significant differences between men and women in the frequency of antibiotic resistance among cases of gonorrhea.

[90] The survey will also be used to inform decision making regarding, for example, appropriate targets and strategies for preventing HAIs and the emergence of antibioticresistant infections.

[91] The survey will collect information about different species of *Acinetobacter* and *Klebsiella*.

[92] Gram-negative infections include those caused by *Klebsiella*, *Acinetobacter*, *Pseudomonas aeruginosa*, and *Escherichia coli*, and are increasingly resistant to most available antibiotics.

[93] CDC also monitors *Clostridium difficile* infections through NHSN.

[94] CDC officials also stated that these data will complement the data on *Clostridium difficile* infections that are collected through NHSN.

[95] CDC officials noted that since more than 90 percent of acute care hospitals (excluding critical access hospitals) participate in CMS's Hospital Inpatient Quality Reporting Program, NHSN data will be more representative by 2012.

[96] See 75 *Fed. Reg.* 50042 (Aug. 16, 2010). Collection and reporting of data on bloodstream infections associated with central lines is required for the fiscal year 2013 payment determination and collection and reporting of surgical site infections is required for the fiscal year 2014 payment determination.

[97] GAO has ongoing work on pharmaceuticals in drinking water.

[98] Treatment plants include, for example, municipal treatment plants that treat domestic sewage as well as healthcare and pharmaceutical manufacturing facility treatment plants.

[99] RCRA's implementing regulations define hazardous waste as including those wastes specifically listed by EPA as well as those wastes exhibiting any of several characteristics.

[100] A hazardous waste generator is any person whose processes and actions produce hazardous waste.

[101] For many contaminants, EPA lacks sufficient information to allow EPA to make a regulatory determination. See GAO, *Safe Drinking Water Act: EPA Should Improve Implementation of Requirements on Whether to Regulate Additional Contaminants,* GAO-11-254 (Washington, D.C.: May 27, 2011).

[102] 74 *Fed. Reg.* 51,850, 51,852 (Oct. 8, 2009).

[103] The other two criteria are: "the contaminant is known to occur, or there is a substantial likelihood that the contaminant will occur, in public water systems with a frequency and at levels of public health concern" and "in the sole judgment of the Administrator, regulation of such a contaminant presents a meaningful opportunity for health risk reduction for persons served by public water systems." 42 U.S.C. §§ 300g-1(b)(1)(A),(b)(1)(B)(ii) (2011).

[104] EPA expects to publish the next CCL by 2014.

[105] In addition, USGS has completed a national study of streambed sediment in about 50 streams that are located in 17 states but the results have not been made available. USGS officials told us that the agency expects to issue a report in 2012. However, some of the data have been published and show, for example, that trimethoprim, an antibiotic, occurred in higher concentrations in streambed sediment, compared to the overlying stream water. See E.T. Furlong et al., "Distributions of Organic Wastewater Contaminants between Water and Sediment in Surface-Water Samples in the United States," *Proceedings of the 3rd*

International Conference on Pharmaceuticals and Endocrine Disrupting Chemicals in Water (2003), pp. 60-62.

[106] The five national studies also measured the presence of the antiseptic active ingredient triclosan in the environment. (For more information on triclosan, see app. IV).

[107] In comparison, EPA's targeted national sewage sludge study sample was designed to be representative of U.S. publicly owned treatment plants that treat more than one million gallons of wastewater per day.

[108] ew antibiotics were detected in groundwater. For example, neither ciprofloxacin nor erythromycin was detected in groundwater. According to USGS officials, while antibiotics were generally less likely to be detected in groundwater compared to surface water systems, the USGS groundwater study's findings document that at least some antibiotics are able to enter groundwater.

[109] Among the national studies of streams, groundwater, and untreated drinking water, the maximum antibiotic concentration level detected was 1.9 micrograms per liter of water—for sulfamethoxazole detected in streams. A concentration level of 1 microgram per liter of water is also referred to as 1 part per billion and a detection level of 1 milligram per liter of water is also referred to as 1 part per million.

[110] iprofloxacin was not detected in the wastewater effluent study. Other antibiotics were detected in the treated effluent samples, including sulfamethoxazole and trimethoprim; the maximum concentration level for sulfamethoxazole was .589 micrograms per liter of water and the maximum concentration level for trimethoprim was .353 micrograms per liter of water.

[111] In addition to the wastewater effluent study, USGS has conducted other, generally smaller-scale studies that examined levels of antibiotics in various sources of human and animal waste. For example, in one study USGS found chlortetracycline concentrations ranging from 68 to 1000 micrograms per liter of swine waste lagoon samples. See Campagnolo et al., "Antimicrobial residues in animal waste and water resources proximal to large-scale swine and poultry feeding operations," *The Science of the Total Environment*, vol. 299 (2002), pp. 89-95.

[112] EPA officials stated that they selected wastewater treatment plants that primarily receive wastewater from municipal sources and that discharge effluent to surface water.

[113] EPA officials stated that while this study will provide the agency with information that will be useful in terms of the occurrence frequency and concentration of erythromycin, additional method development work will be required to produce a method that can be used for regulatory purposes.

[114] Horizontal gene transfer—the process in which bacteria exchange genes that are coded for resistance—can also lead to an increase in the population of antibiotic-resistant bacteria in the environment because bacteria that were previously nonresistant become resistant. Studies have shown that concentrated animal feeding operations and wastewater treatment plants have high densities of antibiotics, as well as antibiotic-resistant bacteria, and that both characteristics facilitate gene transfer. For example, one study found that when swine waste was applied to fertilize soil, resistant bacteria found in the waste transferred their resistance genes to other bacteria in the soil. See H. Heuer et al., "Spreading antibiotic resistance through spread manure: characteristics of a novel plasmid type with low %G+C content," *Environmental Microbiology* (2009), vol. 11, pp. 937-949.

[115] See S. Castiglioni, et al., "Novel homologs of the multiple resistance regulator *mar*A in antibiotic-contaminated environments," *Water Research*, vol. 42 (2008), pp. 4271-4280.

[116] See C.W. Knapp et al., "Indirect Evidence of Transposon-Mediated Selection of Antibiotic Resistance Genes in Aquatic Systems at Low-Level Oxytetracycline Exposures," *Environmental Science & Technology*, vol. 42 (2008), pp. 5348-5353.

[117] See J. Munoz-Aguayo et al., "Evaluating the Effects of Chlortetracycline on the Proliferation of Antibiotic-Resistant Bacteria in a Simulated River Water Ecosystem," *Applied and Environmental Microbiology*, vol. 73 (2007), pp. 5421-5425.

[118] The antibiotic concentration level that is known to increase the population of resistant bacteria because of selective pressure is referred to as a minimum inhibitory concentration (MIC) level. MIC levels are determined for specific types of bacteria and antibiotics and a MIC level reflects the lowest concentration of an antibiotic that prevents visible growth of a bacterium in two types of laboratory tests. MIC levels are used to predict the success or failure of an antibiotic treatment in a clinical setting, and thus, guide healthcare providers' choice of antibiotics to treat bacterial infections. According to a USGS official, the low concentration levels of antibiotics in the environment that have been detected in national studies are generally characterized as such because they are below MIC levels.

[119] USGS officials further stated that there is evidence that antibiotic concentration levels lower than MIC levels can affect, among other things, bacterial growth in the environment. See J.C. Underwood et al., "Effects of the Antimicrobial Sulfamethoxazole on Groundwater Bacterial Enrichment," *Environmental Science and Technology*, vol. 45 (2011), pp. 3096-3101.

[120] For example, see J. Fick et al., "Pharmaceuticals and Personal Care Products in the Environment: Contamination of Surface, Ground, and Drinking Water from Pharmaceutical Production," *Environmental Toxicology and Chemistry*, vol. 28 (2009), pp. 2522-2527. This study showed high concentrations of certain antibiotics in rivers and lakes near a wastewater treatment plant in India that receives wastewater from approximately 90 drug manufacturers. USGS officials told us that they are currently designing a national study of pharmaceutical manufacturing facilities that will examine antibiotic concentration levels in areas proximal to such facilities.

[121] For example, one study, not conducted by USGS, has documented that triclocarban, an antiseptic active ingredient, persists and bioaccumulates in soils amended with treated sewage sludge. See C.P. Higgins et al., "Persistence of Triclocarban and Triclosan in Soils after Land Application of Biosolids and Bioaccumulation in *Eisenia Foetida*," *Environmental Toxicology and Chemistry*, vol. 30 (2010), pp. 556-563.

End Notes for Appendix I

[1] A complete list of search terms was variations on the phrases "antibiotic resistance" or "antimicrobial resistance" found in combination with any of the following terms: "environment," "ground water," "surface water," "drinking water," "waste water," "effluent," "hospital effluent," "municipal sewage," "animal feeding operation," "ecotoxicity," "pharmaceutical plant," "sediment," and "soil."

[2] For the purposes of our literature review, we defined the environment as water, soil, and sediment, as well as certain wastewater treatment-related settings and certain agriculturalrelated settings that serve as pathways into water, soil, and sediment.

End Notes for Appendix II

[1] *Escherichia coli* O157 can also spread through human feces. In addition to consuming contaminated meat, exposure to *Escherichia coli* O157 can occur by consuming other contaminated foods (e.g., milk and lettuce) or by having direct contact with infected carriers.

[2] Bacteria that cause disease are referred to as pathogenic bacteria. In order to cause disease, pathogens must be able to enter the body, which can occur, for example, through the mouth, eyes, or wounds that tear the skin.

[3] Some bacteria have developed resistance to antibiotics naturally, long before the development of commercial antibiotics.

[4] Any use of antibiotics—appropriate and inappropriate—creates selective pressure among bacteria.

[5] A species is a group of organisms—including bacteria—with common traits, such as similar genetic characteristics.

[6] As an example, *Escherichia coli* O157 is a strain of the *Escherichia coli* species.

[7] The resistance gene was found in cases of *Escherichia coli*, *Klebsiella pneumoniae*, and *Enterobacter cloacae* infections. The presence of this particular gene resulted in resistance to certain antibiotics including the carbapenems subclass; for certain bacterial infections, carbapenems are considered antibiotics of last resort.

[8] The Clinical and Laboratory Standards Institute, a nonfederal entity, establishes ranges for the interpretation of test results for antibiotic resistance.

[9] Test values may also fall into ranges for the 'susceptible' and 'intermediate' categories.

End Notes for Appendix IV

[1] Other active ingredients include iodine and chloroxylenol.

[2] In contrast, disinfectants are used on inanimate surfaces or objects to destroy or inactivate infectious microorganisms. Consequently, disinfectants, even if they contain the same active ingredient as an antiseptic, are regulated as chemicals by the Environmental Protection Agency.

[3] Federal Food, Drug, and Cosmetic Act of 1938, codified as amended at 21 U.S.C. § 301 & scattered sections (2011). To be considered a drug, a product must be intended for use in the diagnosis, cure, mitigation, treatment, or prevention of disease in humans or animals, or it must be intended to affect the structure or any function of the body of humans or other animals. Most antiseptic products are currently being marketed under the Tentative Final Monograph for over-the-counter Healthcare Antiseptic Drug Products, published in 1994. See 59 *Fed. Reg.* 31,402 (June 17, 1994).

[4] Since bacteria use similar mechanisms to resist the effects of antiseptics and antibiotics, scientists believe that it may be possible that exposure and development of resistance to antiseptics could also result in resistance to antibiotics.

[5] M. Braoudaki and A.C. Hilton, "Adaptive Resistance to Biocides in *Salmonella enteric* and *Escherichia coli* O157 and Cross-Resistance to Antimicrobial Agents," *Journal of Clinical Microbiology*, Vol. 42 (2004), pp. 73-78.

[6] E.C. Cole, et al., "Investigation of antibiotic and antibacterial agent cross-resistance in target bacteria from homes of antibacterial product users and nonusers," *Journal of Applied Microbiology*, Vol. 95 (2003), pp. 664-676.

[7] Officials from FDA and the Centers for Disease Control and Prevention told us that they do not collect information about the amounts of antiseptics produced or used in the United States. According to FDA officials, however, FDA collects annual drug distribution data for chlorhexidine gluconate products, which are used as topical antiseptics, but are not covered under FDA's monograph for antiseptic drug products.

[8] In addition, USGS has completed a national study of streambed sediment in about 50 streams that are located in 17 states but the results have not been made available. USGS officials told us that the agency expects to issue a report in 2012. According to USGS officials, the national study of streambed sediment also tested for the presence of triclosan.

[9] As part of an ongoing study, EPA and USGS are measuring for the presence of triclosan and triclocarban in treated drinking water. According to EPA officials, findings are expected to be made available sometime in 2012.

[10] According to USGS officials, the laboratory method used for measuring triclosan in the agency's stream study was different than the method used in subsequent USGS studies. USGS officials further stated that this change in methodology resulted in higher triclosan detection frequencies in the stream study, compared to subsequent USGS studies.

[11] Triclosan has been detected in other USGS studies involving human waste sources. For example, see C.A. Kinney et al., "Survey of Organic Wastewater Contaminants in Biosolids Destined for Land Application," *Environmental Science and Technology*, vol. 40 (2006), pp. 7207-7215.

INDEX

A

B

C

F

G

H

I

K

L

M

N

O

P

Q

R

S